together

investing in your marriage

9 session small group resource for married couples

Published 2008 by CWR, Waverley Abbey House, Waverley Lane, Farnham, Surrey GU9 8EP, UK. Registered Charity No. 294387. Registered Limited Company No. 1990308.

FamilyLife is a ministry of Agapé, Fairgate House, Kings Road, Tysley, Birmingham, B11 2AA. Tel: 0121 7654404. Fax: 0121 7654065. Email: info@agape.org.uk Web: www.familylife.uk.com www.agape.org.uk
Agape Ministries Ltd., Registered in England No. 949989. Registered office as above. Charity Reg No 258421.
VAT no 200 1787 10.
Agapé is a member of the Evangelical Alliance and Global Connections, and is part of Campus Crusade for Christ International.

See back of book for list of National Distributors.

Cover image: Gettyimages: PhotoAlto/Sigrid Olsson
Images: Duncan Moore (page 8), all other pictures from PhotoDisc, i-stock and THINKSTOCK

Printed in England by Yeomans Press

ISBN: 978-1-85343-454-7

Contents

Acknowledgements

We want to thank a number of people who have been committed to produce this study and worked so hard over the last three years. You are a great team!

Firstly, we want to thank Ed and Candice Holtz, full-time workers with Campus Crusade for Christ, who had a huge impact on our spiritual lives and growth. We are incredibly grateful for the role you have played in our lives by inviting us to join a couples group to study *Building your Marriage*, one of the HomeBuilder© series, which transformed our marriage! Thank you also for the help and encouragement you gave us as we set about developing *Together*.

We are deeply grateful to Roger and Donna Vann who have brought their invaluable experience in marriage matters and the development of Bible-based resources. Thank you for your creative thinking, your writing skills, constant encouragement and friendship. We are also very grateful to Gary and Jan Palmer, our friends and partners in FamilyLife ministry in the UK. Thank you for your vision, fantastic support and attention to detail! Our friends Antony and Deborah Elliott gave us the benefit of their experience in recovery from divorce and provided significant input to the questions for couples who have been in a previous relationship. Thank you to our friends and colleagues within Agapé: Tony Brown, John and Kate Arkell and Tim and Angie Moyler for their valuable input. We are also grateful to our colleagues in FamilyLife© in the USA, especially Howard Ostendorff and his team at Global Outreach for their encouragement, guidance and practical support.

We are also indebted to the many people who were involved in leading groups for the field-testing of the material in their homes. A big thank you to the dozens of couples across the country who took the time and effort to give us constructive feedback to help us knock this study into shape. Thank you too to David and Esther Wood for organising everything.

There are also many people who have prayed faithfully and given financially to this resource and to support FamilyLife ministry in the UK – thank you so much!

There are a few sources of inspiration for *Together* that need special recognition. We have drawn deeply from the teachings of FamilyLife© USA. We have also used some of the original concepts and ideas developed by Dennis Rainey in *Building your Marriage*, a HomeBuilder© couples Bible study.[1] Many of the optional additional questions for 'remarried couples' were born out of the HomeBuilder© study *Making your Remarriage Last* by Jim Keller. We are very grateful to the authors and to Group Publishing for giving us permission to use their material.

Finally, thanks to Lynette Brooks and her fantastic team at CWR for partnering with us to publish *Together*.

Introduction

Mark: *When I first met Christine I thought she was gorgeous and I tried very hard to impress her. When the jokes didn't work, I pulled out all the stops and took her out for a meal ...*
Christine: *When I first met Mark I thought he was James Bond! He whisked me off on our first date on the back of his enormous motorbike and he looked very sexy in his leather jacket. We were the last to leave the Italian restaurant that night. Three years later we were married.*

Many books and films would end the story at this point with '... and they lived happily ever after'. Those of us who are married know that falling in love is easy, but building a strong and flourishing marriage takes effort. In the early years we had our ups and downs and muddled along, just like many other couples. It was only after ten years of marriage that our relationship started to change, when we joined a small group to study what the Bible had to say about marriage. We – the Daniels – began to communicate in deeper ways, to express our love for one another even when we didn't feel like it, and to resolve conflicts and forgive each other in a new way. Only then did we see that we had been gradually drifting apart.

As we began to understand and apply God's view of marriage, our relationship experienced a transformation. We wanted to share these benefits with other couples, and so (with lots of encouragement and support) each couple from the original group started other small groups with a view to helping marriages.

Years later we began to develop *Together*. This material is the result of three years of development, born out of some ten years' experience in leading small groups for couples and based on many of the principles taught by FamilyLife© in their HomeBuilder© couples series.[1] It has been tested by dozens of couples across the country. Our dream is that groups would multiply throughout the UK and that many couples would experience the grace and power of God in their marriages.

Together **is a nine-session resource on marriage for small groups of couples. It is not a typical 'marriage enrichment' course nor just a Bible study on the topic of marriage. Rather, it helps couples draw closer to God and each other. It unpacks God's plan for marriage and addresses some common 'real life' marriage issues such as improving communication, resolving conflict and expressing love. It is fun ... and challenging.**

This study does require significant commitment, but if you would be willing to dive into the experience as a couple, we are confident you will find that, over the nine sessions, God will make a difference in your marriage which will be visible to all.

Mark & Christine Daniel

NOTES

1. Used with permission. Further Resources (on our website www.togetherinmarriage.com) shows the current range of HomeBuilder © resources available and how to order copies.

How to use this book

You could complete this study alone with your partner, but it is **designed to be used in a small group of four or five couples** for maximum learning benefit, including accountability (if desired).

This resource provides the opportunity to relax together, perhaps over a meal, and discover more for your relationship. **Each group will have a leader couple to organise meetings and facilitate the discussions.** Each session covers a separate topic and includes discussion questions appropriate for a group setting. Private issues are kept for couples to discuss at a separate 'Couple Time' between the sessions. *Together* emphasises practical life application of biblical principles and **is designed to help couples ...**

- **grow closer together** in their love, commitment, understanding and intimacy ... and
- **grow in greater spiritual understanding and practice together;** allowing God to work in their lives, and increasing their dependence upon Him to make them more fruitful as His followers.

There is an Introductory Session which allows couples to meet over a meal and give it a try. If everyone agrees, you can arrange to meet regularly for nine more sessions. The structure of sessions and further details of how they work are covered in the Introductory Session on pages 9–17.

This is a workbook. Each participant will need their own copy if they want to continue meeting after the Introductory Session. Material for the initial meeting can be downloaded from the Internet at www.togetherinmarriage.com

Leading a group

Leading a group is easier than you may think. **There is a separate Leader's Guide to help you get started and prepare for meetings.** The Guide is also packed with supplementary information and tips, such as how to split a session into two meetings if desired.

If you are engaged...

You will be preparing for your wedding day, but also for married life. *Together* is designed to help you build a firm base for your journey through life ... together. Most of the exercises are applicable for all couples, engaged or married, but from time to time **there are alternative questions for those preparing for marriage which can be found on our website** www.togetherinmarriage.com. You will find other support for engaged couples on the website.

If you are remarried...

You may be a 'remarried couple' because **either you or your current partner – or both of you – have previously been married or in a relationship with someone else**. Even the partner who has not been married before is likely to face issues whether the result of death or divorce. Whatever the situation, there will be sensitive, even painful, issues for one or both partners. **There are optional questions at the end of some of the Couple Time sections to help address these issues.**

Divorce is a difficult and vulnerable subject for many people. *Together* does not look at the theology of divorce. Instead, this study encourages couples who have experienced divorce to identify, talk about and positively address the issues they face together, in order to build a strong life-long marriage with their new partner.

The Bible and *Together*

The *Together* resource uses the Bible as its basis. The sessions will help you discover what the Bible has to say about marriage and relationships. You will be able to experience for yourself the application and value of it for your own marriage.

Unless otherwise stated, the New International Version is used, which is a reliable modern translation. However, other excellent translations exist and if you prefer, you can use another Bible version.

Why use the Bible? **The Bible is special because it is 'God-breathed'.** The writer Paul in his letter to Timothy tells us that: *All scripture is God-breathed and is useful for teaching, rebuking, correcting and training in righteousness* (2 Timothy 3:16).
The word for God-breathed is literally translated as 'inspired by God'. The authors from Moses to John are human but the consistent source and inspiration is God's Holy Spirit.

When buying a car we refer to the manufacturer's handbook to help maintain it in good working order. Although as humans we aren't put together on a factory assembly line, we are designed and given life by God. What better manual for dealing with issues of life and relationships than instructions from our Creator? Furthermore, the Bible isn't just a manual for life or a rule-book, but words from a loving God, who wants to have a relationship with us. To read and learn from it can be life-changing.

How will you benefit?

Apart from a transformed marriage, a key benefit is that couples form deep, lasting and supportive friendships. Couples who have taken part in testing *Together* have given us these quotes, which speak for themselves:

'This material has provided a structure and focus for our marriage that has enabled it to grow.'

'The course was very powerful in being able to share the marriage journey with other couples. The regular meals were a wonderful blessing and an integral part of our fellowship!'

'A lot of friends asked, "What you doing a marriage course for, you got problems then?" to which our reply was "Not yet, and hopefully with the group's help it will stay that way!" 'For us the course has given us time to talk about subjects we had skirted round over sixteen years of marriage and ensure they didn't become an issue in the future.'

'We've developed really strong friendships with other couples who we know will support us whatever we go through in our marriage.'

'We have learnt so much together about living Christian marriage with integrity.'

'Marriage is a two-sided ladder. God is at the top of it and we start on the bottom rung of each side. The closer to God we get the closer to each other we become.'

Introductory Session: Making the most of marriage?

Introductory Reading

This session introduces the *Together* study and considers what it takes to build a strong and flourishing marriage. The session will give you a 'taster' for this group study and at the end of the evening you can decide whether you wish to continue.

Ground rules

There are three simple ground rules to ensure the session is an enjoyable time of learning together:

1. Respect each other – Don't share anything that would embarrass your partner or others in the group.
2. Maintain personal boundaries – You can pass on any question you don't want to answer.
3. Be confidential – Whatever is said in the group stays in the group.

Introductions

All parts are optional.

A. Go around and introduce yourselves. Include:

- Number of years married
- Number/ages of any children
- Hobby/sport/special interest or, a little known fact about yourself

B. Go around again with each couple briefly telling either a funny story or something with fond memories about one of the following:[1]

- When and where you met.
- A particular date when you first knew each other.
- A honeymoon experience or something from the early years of your marriage.

Discussion questions

Pick three or four to discuss as a group.

1. What attracted you to your partner when you first met?
2. Name a couple who model a good marriage to you (could be relatives, friends, or you could describe a media couple or TV characters). What is it about the relationship that you like?
3. How do (or how did) your parents influence your view of marriage?
4. What is marriage?
5. What are some of the things that make marriage difficult in today's society?
6. What makes a strong and flourishing marriage?

A vision for marriage

Everyone seems to have their own idea about marriage today. So why marriage? What's it all about anyway?

Rodney and Mabel wondered how there could possibly be more to marriage than this!

It is clear from the Bible that marriage is designed by God and He has a 'vision' for it. His vision gives marriage a purpose and an exciting, practical plan to make it work. When we appreciate how special this relationship is, we will defend it and invest in it. *Together* is a series of nine studies for small groups of couples in all stages of life and circumstances. It unpacks God's plan for marriage and addresses some common 'real life' marriage issues.

Any marriage – whether good or bad – has an impact on the wider community. **We've all noticed the ripple effects of a marriage that's been torn apart. What about the ripple effects of one that is truly alive and kicking?**

No 'group therapy' or embarrassing revelations. Just the opportunity to get together, perhaps over a relaxing meal and **discover more for your relationship and find a renewed vision for your marriage … together!**

Foundation Principle:
A flourishing marriage is one in which both partners have a shared vision and are committed to spending time learning and growing together.

Opportunity to prepare for Couple Time

My thoughts at this point …

Take a moment *by yourself* to think about how the things you have discussed relate to your marriage, so you can talk about it in your Couple Time (after this group meeting).

i. One thing that particularly attracts me to my partner right now is …

– Warm, generous, loving, kind, insightful, understanding, wise, caring, compassionate, easy on the eye, full of character!

ii. What was my vision or mental picture of marriage when we first got married? (Tick any ideas below or write your own.)

- ☐ I want it to be 'happily ever after'
- ☐ This will work as long as …
- ☐ Two children and a dog
- ☐ When we're married I can change him/her
- ☐ We'll stick it, whatever happens 'till death do us part'
- ☐ I want our marriage to be better than my parents' marriage
- ☐ Other …

To love + serve the Lord together.
To walk in his ways together.

iii. What are a few words which would describe how I feel about my marriage now?

– Most important relationship in my life. – thank God for it.
– my wife is very precious – wow.

iv. In what way do I want to see this *Together* group and our 'Couple Times' benefit our relationship?

Not sure – help us reinvent/understand how we can be better disciples of Christ together.

In your Couple Time be prepared to talk about your answers and what you can do to make the most of your Together experience.

A good marriage is the closest thing on earth to the realization of a practical, enduring, and loving coexistence between people. It is a sign, a spiritual and social and political example, of depths of love and patience and forgiveness that are unknown in other spheres of life.

Mike Mason,
The Mystery of Marriage

What is *Together* and what do we do?

This is not a typical marriage enrichment course nor just a Bible study on the topic of marriage. Rather, it attempts to help couples lay a lasting spiritual foundation and includes elements of discipleship.[2] Many practical marriage issues are covered as well with a focus on couples taking specific action 'steps'. Each topic is anchored in biblical principles.

Together is structured as follows:

- You will begin each evening with an **informal time of hospitality** (eg 7–8 pm)
- Following on is the **Group Session** of 100 minutes (eg 8.00–9.40 pm) which is designed to stimulate discussion on the topic and Scripture.
- A **Couple Time** of 60 minutes is completed privately at a time between the group meetings to discuss and apply what is relevant to your marriage.
- There is no written preparation for group meetings but you are asked to complete the **Introductory Reading** (5–10 minutes) to prepare for the topic before you come.
- We recommend that you **meet every two weeks,** with flexibility for holiday periods.

Session	Title
1	Growing even closer through our communication
2	Finding unity through God's purpose and plan for marriage
3	Expressing love through emotional intimacy
4	Facing life's relationship challenges with God
5	Handling our feelings constructively
6	Living positively with our differences
7	Deepening our physical and spiritual intimacy
8	Fitting together as husbands and wives
9	Leaving a legacy that will last forever

… And finally

Shall we continue meeting? Some things to discuss:

- One venue or rotate?
- Include a meal or not? (bring & share; rotating hosts …?)
- Childcare needs?
- Putting all nine sessions in the diary …
- Confirming start and finish times.

Arrange a Couple Time. Make time for each other after this session for your Couple Time, to talk through and apply what is relevant to your lives.

Marriage is the alliance of two people, one of whom never remembers birthdays and the other who never forgets them.

Ogden Nash

Why not agree a date now and note it here:

Couple Time

As you talk to each other remember the dos and don'ts of listening:

Don't	Do
• Interrupt. • Be distracted. • Criticise or blame – instead say how you feel. • Give unwanted advice. • Change the subject.	• Listen actively – give your full attention. • Be sensitive to one another as you share your thoughts and feelings ... this is important. • Speak the truth in love. • Try to understand – from time to time check your understanding by 'feeding back' to your partner what you think he/she has said. • Be ready to apologise for any attitudes or behaviour that has caused your partner to feel marginalised or misunderstood.

If you didn't have time to complete the Couple Time preparation box during your group meeting then take a few minutes to fill it in now before you talk to your partner. As you talk, consider elaborating upon what you wrote or ticked in the box. Also talk about any insights you gained from the group discussion. There are optional additional questions at the end for couples who are remarried (turn to page 16).

My thoughts at this point ...

Take turns explaining your answers for **i, ii, iii** and **iv**

Following on from your answers to question **iv** identify some personal goals or areas you want to grow in your marriage. Try to be specific, eg communicate more openly, understand my partner better and how I can show him/her love, talk more openly about my feelings, manage my temper better, liven up our sex life! (NB you won't be asked to share these goals with anyone in the group.) Write down at least three goals.

Personal goals

- Understand my wife better.
- Be more loving/less selfish/selfcentred.
- Be less 'busy'

At the next group meeting you will be asked to share one insight or encouragement that has resulted from the Introductory Session or your Couple Time discussion. Agree with your partner the insight/encouragement to be shared with the group.

My insight:

Before you come to the next group meeting please complete the Introductory Reading for Session 1: **Growing even closer through our communication** (pages 19–20). It will set you up well for the group meeting and only takes approximately five minutes to read. Most of us would like to be better at communicating. How do we communicate in ways that lead to greater understanding and grow a closer relationship?

For remarried couples

(optional additional questions)

For couples where either one or both partners have previously been married or in a long-term relationship.[3]

i. In what ways has your previous relationship, or the previous relationship of your partner, affected your expectations of this marriage?

ii. Is there anything that you fear might affect this marriage, which may (or may not) have happened in your previous marriage, or that of your partner?

iii. Agree on one thing you could do **to support your partner** as you face any challenges together.

Identify a personal action point for you as an individual (a specific way to follow through with an action from any insights you gained from the discussion with your partner).

Personal action point:

NOTES

1. Adapted from 'Getting to Know You' Session 1, *Building Your Marriage*, Group Publishing Copyright © 2000 Dennis Rainey. Used with permission.
2. A Christian disciple is someone who follows Jesus, literally a lifelong learner of His ways.
3. Questions adapted from 'Expectations in Remarriage' Session 1, *Making Your Remarriage Last*, Group Publishing Copyright © 2001 Jim Keller. Used with permission.

1

Growing even closer through our communication

Introductory Reading

Today we can communicate faster, with more people, and in many more ways than ever before – mobile telephones, email and text messages, to name a few. Yet in spite of all our technology, we know **communication is more than just transmitting a message between one person and another – it's about understanding and building a close connection.** Good communication in marriage is essential. So what gets in the way – what makes us feel disconnected?

What are the things that make communication difficult for me and my partner?

Feeling disconnected?

There are many reasons for feeling disconnected from our partner, including:

I. **Lack of time and energy.** Busyness and stress so fill most people's lives today that many couples complain they simply haven't got enough time for each other. Living in the fast lane also drains our emotional batteries. It's no wonder our relationships suffer.

II. **Our differences.** Family backgrounds, experiences during childhood, personalities, value systems and religious beliefs all affect how we think and respond to situations. Our gender differences may also cause misunderstandings. Generally speaking, women like to express their feelings and men prefer to share information.

III. **Styles of expression.** Some prefer to talk about facts and concrete realities, whereas others focus on concepts, ideas and possibilities. An introverted personality often prefers small groups and time alone, whereas extroverts get their energy from interaction with more people. Some like analysing situations before making decisions; others let their hearts rule.

God's design for couples

In the creation account we read that God makes humans 'in his image', as male and female.[1] We also read about His design for marriage: that two should leave their families, unite, and become one. A new unit is formed as we join our hearts, minds and bodies in marriage. God now sees us as 'one'. We are still individuals but somehow, together, we have become something new – a unique expression of the image of God.

For this reason a man will leave his father and mother and be united to his wife, and they will become one flesh. The man and his wife were both naked, and they felt no shame.
Genesis 2:24–25

Communication helps us to get close to our partner – to build emotional intimacy and to experience and develop our 'oneness'. Busyness, stress and our differences can make communication difficult, even though that's not what we intend. **But the root of communication problems lies in the distortion of God's design.** We have an inner bent towards putting our own thoughts, feelings, desires and our lives at the centre of everything and before others. The Bible calls this sin. We also tend to hide our true selves from each other. This makes it difficult to get close to our partner.

How do I overcome my self-centredness and connect deeply with the thoughts, feelings and desires of my partner?

Good communication

We can build understanding and get closer to our partner by improving our communication skills. We can learn to be better listeners, to express ourselves more clearly, understand body language and the like, but at the end of the day these are only tools.

The heart of deep communication is about being transparent, which requires complete openness and trust.[2] There should be nothing to hide and no secrets to undermine the bond of trust. Transparent communication is free from shame, blame and fear. This level of sharing is a great challenge, but together – with God's help – we can work to see our communication become something that brings joy, closeness and new energy to our marriage.

This session looks at how we can develop a closer relationship through the way we communicate.

Ground rules

Remember the three simple ground rules to ensure the session is an enjoyable time of learning together:

1. Respect each other – Don't share anything that would embarrass your partner or others in the group.
2. Maintain personal boundaries – You can pass on any question you don't want to answer.
3. Be confidential – Whatever is said in the group stays in the group.

Group session

Feedback

- What insights or encouragements did you gain from your Couple Time?
- Was there anything in the Introductory Reading for this session about communication that prompted you to think about the subject in a new way? Explain.

A How are we communicating?

We all have different ways of communicating depending on our personalities and experiences. **As couples we tend to develop patterns of communication which can become habits, for good or bad.** Also, our modern way of life can squeeze out time for each other. If we want to grow a close relationship we need to be able to communicate well. This will mean dealing with those things that might prevent it happening.

Chris and Carol

Chris and Carol have had a long, hard day. At last the children are in bed and Carol settles down to watch the television

Chris: *(cheerfully)* I noticed that new people moved in across the road. Maybe we should invite them over for a drink tomorrow evening?

Carol: Mmm ... if you like.

Chris: Or we could invite them for dinner or a BBQ at the weekend? We could invite Brenda and Harry next door too – we haven't seen them for ages. It would be good to do something fun ... you know what they say about all work and no play ...

Carol: *(not really listening)* OK.

Chris: Sales are down again this month ... that's two bad months. People are getting nervous ... there's talk of redundancies. *(Pauses for a moment)* Carol, I don't think you're listening to me.

Carol: What?! *(reasonably gently)* Look, Chris, I'm trying to watch this. Can we talk about work later?

Chris: When does it finish? I've been wanting to talk to you all week … I was hoping to get an early night tonight … after all, this is Friday night!

He looks at her intently hoping she'll get the hint.

Carol: *(Glued to the TV and not even looking up)* OK – I'll see you later love.

Chris: Carol, that's not what I'm saying, I …

Carol: *(Interrupting)* I'm sorry Chris. I just want a bit of time to wind down. Is that a problem? I've had people, meetings and decisions all day long and it's just nice to come home and switch off from everything. Would you mind making me a coffee while you're up, please? We can talk later, OK?

Chris doesn't reply but leaves quietly for the kitchen to make drinks. He returns and hands Carol a coffee. For a moment he hesitates as if to say something, but doesn't and then moves towards the door.

Chris: Don't wake me when you come up.

He leaves, closing the door behind him.

Carol: *(To herself.)* At last, some peace …

She pushes away thoughts about the look of disappointment and hurt on Chris's face as he left, and tries to enjoy her TV programme.

1. What do you notice about Chris and Carol's communication – good and bad?

2. If this were a typical pattern of interaction, how would it affect their relationship? What could they do differently to improve communication?

Foundation Principle:
Good communication means making our marriage partner a priority.

Opportunity to prepare for Couple Time

A How are we communicating?

Take a moment by yourself to prepare for your Couple Time by thinking about how you communicate in your marriage.

Note three things that you want to talk to your partner about:

i. an area where our communication is working well.

ii. an area where some change might be helpful.

iii. a practical idea to help me make regular time and energy for good communication.

In your Couple Time be prepared to talk about your answers and what you can do to help each other communicate better.

B Communicating at deeper levels

1. What do you think might make communication within a Christian marriage distinctive?

Creation design

The heart that breaks open can contain the whole universe.
Joanna Macy

In the creation account in Genesis we read that God makes marriage part of His design for human relationships. **His plan for marriage is a level of intimacy between husband and wife in which the two are so close that they are 'one'.**[3] This requires open communication at deeper levels. The apostle Paul affirms the general principle in the New Testament to **open wide your hearts.**[4]

2. The following diagram[5] (page 24) shows different levels of communication. Each level requires different degrees of openness (transparency) and of trust. Think of some examples of potential communication between Chris and Carol for each of the five levels.

Communication level	Degree of openness and trust increases moving through levels 1 to 5	Meaning
1. Cliché	↓	Non-sharing
2. Fact		Sharing what you KNOW
3. Opinion		Sharing what you THINK
4. Emotion		Sharing what you FEEL
5. Transparency		Sharing WHO YOU ARE

3. Many marriages can 'tick over' from day to day with communication rarely going below level 3, like 'marriage business partners' getting on with all that needs to be done. This can lead to a shallow or unsatisfying relationship.

- What is the role of listening in reaching deeper levels of communication?

Don't knock the weather; nine-tenths of people couldn't start a conversation if it didn't change once in a while.

Kin Hubbard

The root of communication problems

Adam and Eve, the first couple, are described as being 'naked and without shame'.[6] Then, in Genesis 3, Adam and Eve doubt God's loving provision for them. They disobey His instructions, giving in to temptation and eating the forbidden fruit. In this symbolic act God's authority is challenged and the whole created order is corrupted with far-reaching consequences. Enter: shame, blame and fear. They hide from God. They also hide from each other – **the openness that once existed between Adam and Eve turns to hiding behind coverings made of fig leaves.**

4. God intends couples to be 'naked and without shame'.

- What do you think this means for the way we communicate as a couple?
- Why do we tend to hide our true selves from each other?

Foundation Principle:
Good communication means growing in deeper understanding, which requires openness and trust.

B Communicating at deeper levels

i. Think about the following statements and how they express your thoughts and feelings. Put your initials somewhere on the line to reflect how you see the issue.

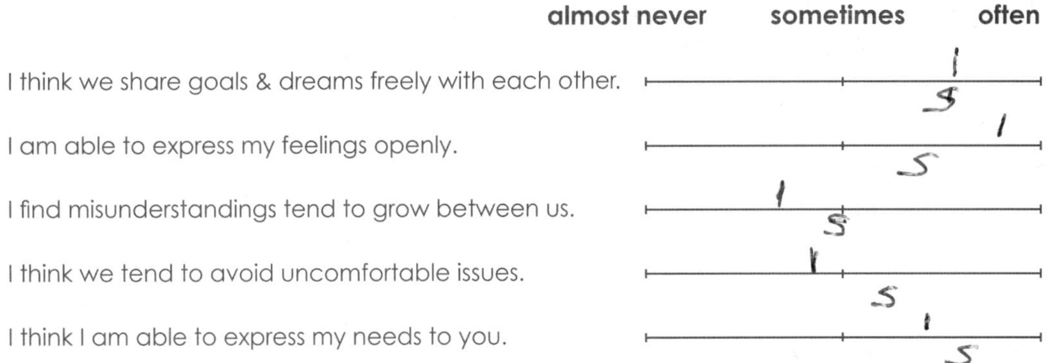

almost never
sometimes
often
I think we share goals & dreams freely with each other.
I am able to express my feelings openly.
I find misunderstandings tend to grow between us.
I think we tend to avoid uncomfortable issues.
I think I am able to express my needs to you.

ii. Now put your partner's initials somewhere to describe how *you think* your partner currently sees the issue.

In your Couple Time be prepared to talk to your partner and explain why you placed your initials where you did.

C Growing in trust and openness

Since the 'Fall' in Genesis 3, relationships have been corrupted by fear. We fear punishment from God because of our sin, so we hide from Him. Other kinds of fears affect our relationships with people – fear of rejection, fear of being hurt – and so we may hide from them.

God reveals who He is – with total transparency – through Jesus. We do not need to fear punishment from God because He showed us His unconditional love by sending Jesus to die for us. His sacrifice dealt with sin and restored our damaged relationship with Himself. **The good news of the gospel is that it can set us free to live the way God intended as husband and wife.**

There is no fear in love. But perfect love drives out fear, because fear has to do with punishment. The one who fears is not made perfect in love.
1 John 4:18

Once we are sure that God will not punish or reject us, we can respond by coming out of hiding. As we begin to trust Him more we will be able to increasingly open ourselves up to Him. This new pattern of communication with God can have a knock-on effect on our communication with our partner.

1. In what ways can a relationship of growing trust and openness with God affect the communication in our marriages?

Foundation Principle:
As we become more secure in God's unconditional love for us, we will be able to communicate more openly as a couple.

C Growing in trust and openness

i. What could I say to my partner to affirm him/her? How much do I trust him/her? Write down something positive below.

Totally. S, you are very trustworthy – but not with [illegible] apples?

ii. How free do I feel to open myself up to God – how much do I trust Him?

[illegible] – totally [illegible]

In your Couple Time be prepared to talk about your answers and what you can do to help each other to grow in openness and trust in your communication, with God and with each other.

… And finally

Take a minute to review the Foundation Principles for the session.

Agree on a date for your diaries for your Couple Time. Make an hour for each other between group meetings to talk through and apply what is relevant to your lives.

Couple Time date:

Good communication is as stimulating as black coffee and just as hard to sleep after.
Anne Morrow Lindberg

Couple Time – 60 minutes

As you talk to each other remember the dos and don'ts of listening:

Don't

- Interrupt.
- Be distracted.
- Criticise or blame – instead say how you feel.
- Give unwanted advice.
- Change the subject or tell your own story.

Do

- Listen actively – give your full attention.
- Be sensitive to one another as you share your thoughts and feelings … this is important.
- Speak the truth in love.
- Try to understand – from time to time check your understanding by 'feeding back' to your partner what you think he/she has said.
- Be ready to apologise for any attitudes or behaviour that has caused your partner to feel marginalised or misunderstood.

If you didn't have time to complete the Couple Time preparation boxes during your group meeting then take a few minutes to fill them in now before you talk to your partner.

A How are we communicating?

Take turns reading out and expanding on your written answers to all three questions on page 23.

Identify a personal action point for you as an individual (a specific way to follow through with an action from any insights you gained from the discussion in the group and/or with your partner). These are intended to be helpful prompts for change if needed.

Personal action point:

Note: Be gentle with each other as you talk about deeper levels of communication. Make a point of affirming your love and acceptance for your partner at whatever level they try to express themselves. Encourage them with your gratitude when moving to a deeper level than you would normally communicate.

B Communicating at deeper levels

Each explain why you placed the initials where you did on page 25, and remember to highlight the things you are doing well.

Identify a personal action point to enable you to communicate at a deeper level, if appropriate.

Personal action point:

Look at Together Notes: Poor Listening/Good Listening (www.togetherinmarriage.com) for more on communication.

C Growing in our trust and openness

Talk about how you can grow in trust and openness in your relationship. Both share your answers to the first question on page 26 before moving on to the second question. Identify an action point if needed.

Personal action point:

Note: If you struggle with past experiences and how these affect your ability to trust your partner, you may consider talking to a trusted friend or counsellor.

At the next group meeting you will be asked to describe one way you are starting to communicate differently with your partner as a result of the session. Agree on one thing you would be prepared to share with the group from your Couple Time and write it down:

Before the next group meeting please complete the Introductory Reading for Session 2: **Finding unity through God's purpose and plan for marriage** (pages 31–33). God designed marriage and He has an exciting purpose and plan for it. Understanding God's plan for our marriages will enable us to find a commitment to a shared vision.

For further reading:

A Child No More, Mary Pytches (London: Hodder & Stoughton, 1991)

Dying to Change, Mary Pytches (London: Hodder & Stoughton, 1996)

For remarried couples

(optional additional questions)

For couples where either one – or both partners – have previously been married or in a long-term relationship.[7]

i. Do you face any special challenges in establishing trust and openness with each other in the light of the previous relationship of either one – or both – partners? How do they affect you?

ii. Agree on one thing you could do to support your partner as you face any challenges together.

Identify a personal action point, if needed.

Personal action point:

NOTES

1. Genesis 1:26–27.
2. Adapted from *Understanding: Communication I*, FamilyLife USA *'Weekend To Remember'* conference manual, revised 1/04. Used with permission.
3. Genesis 2:24.
4. 2 Corinthians 6:11–13.
5. Based on table 'Why am I afraid to tell you who I am' by John Powell, FamilyLife USA *'Weekend to Remember'* conference manual, revised 1/04. Used with permission.
6. Genesis 2:25.
7. Adapted from Question 3, Session 3, *'Making Your Remarriage Last'*, Group Publishing, Copyright © 2001 Jim Keller. Used with permission.

2 Finding unity through God's purpose and plan for marriage

Introductory Reading

You only have to look at the divorce statistics to see that marriage just isn't working for many today. Everyone seems to have their own ideas about how marriage should work, yet it is clear from the Bible that marriage is designed by God. **When we appreciate how special this relationship is, we will defend it and invest in it; and the more we invest, the more valuable it will become.** When we understand God's purpose for marriage, we are in a better position to build the foundations needed to weather the inevitable storms that will come our way. We will also find greater unity as we live together with a shared purpose.

Is our relationship made up of two disconnected individuals or one unified couple?

In the beginning

The pinnacle of God's creation was humankind, because God chose to make human beings 'in His image'.[1] He put the man into His world to work it and take care of it.[2] But God did not intend man to be alone or fulfil his responsibilities on his own.[3] He needed a companion and a 'helper'[4]... woman.

As Adam named the animals,[5] it became clear that no creature could be such a 'helper' for him. Perhaps it was while the animals were pairing off that he recognised what God had known all along.[6] **Adam didn't need a clone of himself; but someone to whom he could relate.** He needed someone who would fill his solitude as well as work alongside him; someone who was both like him and yet different. God presented him with a woman and he received her with delight and excitement! Here was someone who was made of the same 'stuff'. 'Not made out of his head to top him, not out of his feet to be trampled upon by him, but out of his side to be equal with him, under his arm to be protected, and near his heart to be loved.'[7]

Adam and Eve were the first married couple and God blessed them.

God blessed them and said to them, 'Be fruitful and increase in number; fill the earth and subdue it. Rule over the fish of the sea and the birds of the air and over every living creature that moves on the ground.'
Genesis 1:28

God's plan for marriage

God has a plan for marriage, for two individuals to be united as one.[8] He intends for the oneness to be expressed in a unique pair-bond, which is physical, emotional and spiritual. It means being completely open with each other, totally trusting and unashamed before one another in the way we communicate (covered in Session 1) and live together. It also means being clear **why** we are together and **in which direction we are heading so that we are living as a united team**.

Rodney wasn't at all sure that God had anything to do with his marriage

God's purpose for marriage

When we enter into marriage we enter into something God has already designed for a purpose. He intends marriage to be:

I. **the first building block for community life.** We are not meant to be alone. Marriage means two people committing themselves to each other, making a binding covenant with the intention to stay together permanently. It is a commitment to be faithful to one another and to give 100% of ourselves.

II. **a signpost to point people to God.** God made humans to 'mirror His image' on earth – to reflect His character and influence in the way we live and in the nature of our relationship. We point people to God (or not!) through our lifestyles at home, at work and in the community. We also show people what God is like through the nature of our relationship. God made two distinctly different creatures – male and female. It is when these two different humans come together in marriage that a unique aspect of God's character is displayed. Our relationship can actually illustrate for the world the nature of God's love.

What do people see in the way we – as a couple – carry out our responsibilities to steward our time, money and creation?

III. **a way to multiply a godly legacy.** God gave us a responsibility to 'fill' the earth. His desire is for us to have children, and for the family to be a training ground for life. But filling the earth is more than just increasing the number of humans. It is about helping others, including our children, to know God and make Him known. A couple will leave a lasting spiritual legacy as they model God's love and as they tell people about Him – as His ambassadors.

God knows that when the first flush of romantic glow of being in love begins to fade, we will need something outside of ourselves, beyond a cosy relationship, to fire up passion for marriage. God gives us a purpose and plan which draws us together in the way we're meant to be – living life to the full as a couple.

... good marriages are the foundation of society. They are seeds, or cell groups, pointing the way to man's great dream of utopia, which is fundamentally his urgent longing for the kingdom of God.

Mike Mason,
The Mystery of Marriage

This session looks at how we can develop unity through understanding God's purpose and plan for marriage.

Group Session

Feedback

- What insights or encouragements did you gain from your Couple Time following the Communication session?
- Was there anything in the Introductory Reading for this session about God's plan that prompted you to think about the subject in a new way? Explain.

A Finding unity in marriage

We are two different people who need to learn to live together as a united team. Even if we've been married many years there may still be things that get in the way of being a cohesive husband and wife team.

1. What does unity in a marriage actually mean? Consider:

- What kinds of things work against unity in a marriage?
- What kinds of things build unity?

A Finding unity in marriage

i. Note down a few words I could say to my partner to affirm how close I feel to him/her.

ii. Am I struggling with anything **within myself** (not with my partner!) at the moment that could be causing disunity in our marriage? What might need to change so there is greater unity in the marriage?

In your Couple Time be prepared to talk about your answers and how you can support each other in building unity in your marriage.

My most brilliant achievement was my ability to persuade my wife to marry me.

Winston Churchill

B God's purpose and plan for marriage

People have many different ideas about how marriage should work. But the Bible tells us that marriage was designed by God. **God gives us an exciting vision – purposes and a plan – for marriage.** Put simply, His purposes for marriage are:

- to be the first building block for community life,
- to be a signpost to point people to God, and
- to provide a way to multiply a godly legacy.

God's purposes for marriage give it meaning and focus beyond ourselves. **He also gives us a plan – a sort of 'how to' guide to make marriage work** (covered in the rest of this session).

Foundation Principle:
We find unity through the shared vision of fulfilling God's purpose and plan for marriage.

Bible study

15The LORD God took the man and put him in the Garden of Eden to work it and take care
of it. 16And the LORD God commanded the man, 'You are free to eat from any tree in the
garden; 17but you must not eat from the tree of the knowledge of good and evil, for when
you eat of it you will surely die.'
18The LORD God said, 'It is not good for the man to be alone. I will make a helper
suitable for him.'
19Now the LORD God had formed out of the ground all the beasts of the field and all the birds
of the air. He brought them to the man to see what he would name them; and whatever
the man called each living creature, that was its name. 20So the man gave names to all the
livestock, the birds of the air and all the beasts of the field.
But for Adam no suitable helper was found. 21So the LORD God caused the man to fall into
a deep sleep; and while he was sleeping, he took one of the man's ribs and closed up the
place with flesh. 22Then the LORD God made a woman from the rib he had taken out of the
man, and he brought her to the man.
23The man said,

'This is now bone of my bones
and flesh of my flesh;
she shall be called 'woman',
for she was taken out of man.

[24]For this reason a man will leave his father and mother and be united to his wife, and they will become one flesh.
[25]The man and his wife were both naked, and they felt no shame.
Genesis 2:15–25

NOTES ON PASSAGE

2:18 'Helper', Hebrew: *knedgedu*, meaning 'opposite against', an equal who supports one who needs help. 'Suitable', means being like another, matching him and complementary.

2:21 Rib', Hebrew: *sela*, meaning 'side'.

2:23 The Hebrew for 'this is now' is an ecstatic expression meaning 'wow'!
'Man', Hebrew: *Ish*
'Woman', Hebrew: *Ishah*, the feminine form of man's own name.

2:24 'One flesh' is a bonding of 'personhood', established through a sexual, emotional and spiritual union.

1. In the passage God says, *'It is not good for the man to be alone. I will make a helper suitable for him.'* (v.18)

- What does this show us about God?

2. God presents the woman to the man as if she were a gift (v.22).

- What was Adam's reaction? (v.23)

- What do you think attracted him when he saw her?

- Why do you think Adam accepted Eve? On what basis did he receive her?

Note:
Ever since the Fall in Genesis 3, God's perfect creation has been distorted by sin which affects all our relationships. Jesus dealt with sin and helps us to live according to God's plan for marriage.

3. We build a foundation for unity in our marriage when we accept our partner as a 'gift'.

- What does it mean in practice for one marriage partner to receive the other as a gift from God?

- What are the implications for our marriage relationship if we trust that God knew what He was doing when He brought us together?

Foundation Principle:
We can fully accept our partner as God's perfect gift, based on God's character and trustworthiness.

B God's purpose and plan for marriage

i. How does it make me think and feel towards my partner as I reflect on the idea that he/she is a gift from God? (tick any that apply and/or write your own ideas)

- ☐ Gives me a whole new perspective.
- ☑ Produces joy/gratitude towards God.
- ☐ Causes me to question God.
- ☐ Makes me reconsider some of my actions/attitudes towards my partner.
- ☐ Helps me to accept him/her as he/she is.
- ☐ Gives me a deeper appreciation for my partner.
- ☐ Not sure.
- ☐ Other …

In your Couple Time be prepared to talk about your answers and how this concept makes you feel towards your partner and towards God.

Adam and Eve had an ideal marriage. He didn't have to hear about all the men she could have married, and she didn't have to hear about the way his mother cooked.
Kimberley Broyles

C Three building blocks for a strong marriage

God's plan for marriage is a **lifelong process**. He gives us some practical instructions: *'For this reason a man will leave his father and mother and be united to his wife, and they will become one flesh'* (v.24). These building blocks are not just for newlyweds!

Leaving

1. What do you think it means to leave our father and mother? Are there other ties we might need to leave?

2. Why is it important to leave ties?

Being united

3. The phrase *'be united to his wife'* is sometimes translated as *'cleave to his wife'*. What the words of these phrases are trying to convey is a sense of irrevocable commitment; a promise of unbroken covenant faithfulness.

- What does this kind of permanent bonding between two people look like practically?
- What are some of the benefits of this kind of commitment? What are the challenges?

Becoming one flesh

4. The Hebrew word for 'one flesh' refers to the bonding of the **whole** of a human being to another, rather than **just** the sexual aspect of human nature.

- What are some ways a couple can experience greater oneness in a marriage?

Marriage is a wonderful invention: then again, so is a bicycle repair kit.
Billy Connolly

Foundation Principle:
We build a strong marriage as we follow God's plan to leave, be united and grow in oneness.

C Three building blocks for a strong marriage

What new insights into God's plan for marriage have I personally gained which could help me strengthen my marriage?

i. Leaving:

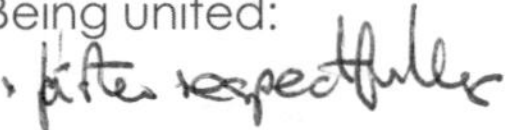

ii. Being united:

iii. Becoming one flesh:

In your Couple Time be prepared to talk about your insight and a way you can follow through with an action to grow together in your marriage.

... And finally

Take a minute to review the Foundation Principles for the session.

Agree on a date in your diaries for your Couple Time:

Couple Time – 60 minutes

Marriages are made in heaven. But, again, so are thunder, lightning, tornados and hail.

Anon

As you talk to each other **remember the dos and don'ts of listening**.

A Finding unity in marriage

Talk about building greater unity in your marriage. Share your answers to the first point on page 34. Then share your answers to the second question, if you completed it. (Note: this is not a question about finding faults in your partner!)

Identify a personal action point. (Remember: action points are intended to be helpful prompts for change **if** needed.)

Personal action point:

· Pray together

· Listen/understand her better.

B God's purpose and plan for marriage

Talk about how it makes you think and feel towards your partner as you reflect on the idea that he/she is a gift from God. In what ways do you (or can you) demonstrate to your partner that you accept him/her unconditionally?

Identify a personal action point.

Personal action point:

Remember S – gift from God.

Continue praying together

Be positive + encouraging.

C Three building blocks for a strong marriage

Share the insights you gained into God's plan for marriage. What are you doing well? How could you follow through with an action to build a stronger marriage?

Personal action point:

There are optional questions for couples who are remarried (page 42) and for those with children (page 43).

At the next group meeting you will be asked to share one new insight you have gained about God's plan for marriage and how this is helping you in your marriage. Agree upon what you would be prepared to share with the group from your Couple Time – maybe a different insight for each of you – and write it down:

Before the next group meeting please complete the Introductory Reading for Session 3: **Expressing love through emotional intimacy** (pages 45–47). We grow closer – and build 'oneness' – when we understand and meet the needs of our partner.

For further reading:

Don't They Make a Lovely Couple, John and Ann Benton (Christian Focus, 2005).

The Mystery of Marriage, Mike Mason (Multnomah Publishers, 1985). Beautifully written and filled with life-transforming insights.

Marriage. Sex in the Service of God, Christopher Ash (InterVarsity Press, 2003). Deep theology and a helpful book for those who want to understand what the Bible has to say in greater depth. The author explores some of the complex and controversial issues, taking a thoughtful approach.

For remarried couples

(optional additional questions)

Take some time to reflect, then talk together. Be gentle. It's a good idea to pray first and ask God for wisdom and sensitivity.

i. Many factors can cause stress and problems for couples where one – or both – partners have been in a previous relationship. These will make leaving old ties – or unravelling them – and being united in a new marriage, difficult unless handled positively. Mark any from the following list that affect you **'Y'** and/or your partner **'P'**.

	Y	**P**
Former spouses (you and/or your partner may have been	☐	☐
divorced or bereaved)	☐	☐
Children from a previous marriage who live with you	☐	☐
Children from a previous marriage who do **not** live with you	☐	☐
Financial support for a previous wife and children	☐	☐
Time – visiting children/holidays	☐	☐
In-laws from previous marriages	☐	☐

ii. Discuss with your partner the stress factors you struggle with most. How do they affect you and your marriage? Do any of them work against unity in your relationship?

iii. What can you do to support your partner in dealing with any of the above? Identify a personal action point, if appropriate.

For couples with children

(optional additional questions)

i. In what ways does having children build – or challenge – the unity in your marriage?

ii. Does anything need to change? Identify a personal action point, if required.

NOTES

1. Genesis 1:26.
2. Genesis 1:28; Genesis 2:15.
3. Genesis 2:18.
4. Hebrew: *knegedu*, a helper suitable for him, or matching him.
5. Genesis 2:19–20.
6. Genesis 2:21–23.
7. *Commentary on the Whole Bible*, Matthew Henry (Marshall, Morgan and Scott, 1961).
8. Genesis 2:24.

3 Expressing love through emotional intimacy

Introductory Reading

In the early stages of attraction between a man and a woman we say they are 'falling in love'. Experts now tell us that this intense emotional period is accompanied by chemical changes in the brain. Each person experiences an unusually high level of tolerance towards the other: their love is literally blind. The problem is that this kind of love is only temporary, typically lasting up to three years. **Couples need to develop a more lasting kind of love once the 'blind love' has run its course.**

Is my love for my partner focused on getting what I need, or on giving them what they need? Do I accept them just the way they are, or does my love depend on how I am feeling or how they are behaving?

Some realities about human love

The love we experience from day to day often depends on:

I. **feelings.** These can be the heady emotions associated with being in love, but they will eventually dry up. Love tends to depend on our mood: *I'm having a good day ... so I feel like loving him/her.*

II. **'my' priorities.** Our love tends to be self-centred because at the centre of human love is the human self – our natural tendency to put our own feelings, desires and thoughts first: *will he/she love me back, look after my needs, give me sex?*

III. **performance.** We are concerned with whether our partner meets the standards we have set: *does he/she deserve my love?*

The problem with human love is that ultimately it is a **taking** kind of love. **Lasting intimate relationships need giving love which is actively other-centred, accepting and unconditional.** But where can we find this love that puts our partner's needs above our own?

There is a greater love, an unselfish love: the love that God shows us. The Bible tells us that God **is** love and that His love is focused on others and serves others.[1]

Rodney wasn't sure Mabel would want to watch the cup final on her birthday

Jesus showed us what God's love is like

God's love is:

- **a decision** … not a feeling.
- **unconditional** … accepts a person as they are.
- **unselfish** … puts the other person's needs first.
- **sacrificial** … gives up rights.
- **active** … takes the initiative to show loving behaviour towards others.

Love is patient, love is kind. It does not envy, it does not boast, it is not proud. It is not rude, it is not self-seeking, it is not easily angered, it keeps no record of wrongs. Love does not delight in evil but rejoices with the truth. It always protects, always trusts, always hopes, always perseveres.
1 Corinthians 13:4–7

Is it possible to love my partner in the way God does?

The New Testament word for this **other-centred love is *agape*.**

Agape love might seem impossible to attain. **Yet God wants to give us love – agape love – to 'pour it into our hearts'.**[2] He is its source, and He has more than enough to spare! The more we open ourselves to God's love, in the context of a relationship with Him, the more His Spirit living within us will fill us with His love. This ***agape*** love will then begin to spill over into the lives of our spouse, our children (if we have them) and those around us. **We can only give this special kind of love when we have first received it from Him.**[3] The impact of ***agape*** love extends far beyond our own marriage and points people to God, fulfilling one of His purposes for marriage.

There is only one being who loves perfectly, and that is God, yet the New Testament distinctly states that we are to love as God does; so the first step is obvious. If ever we are going to have perfect love in our hearts we must have the very nature of God in us.
Oswald Chambers

... marriage inevitably becomes the flagship of all other relationships. One's home is the place where love must first be practiced before it can truly be practiced anywhere else.
Mike Mason,
The Mystery of Marriage

Designed to love

Everyone needs relationships. We are not meant to live as independent beings – **love can only be expressed in relation to others.** We all need the intimacy that comes from deeply knowing and being known by another person. **God created us to be in relationships – with Him but also with other people – to give and receive love.** In marriage, the most intimate of all human relationships, God intends each partner to complement and complete the other with ***agape*** love. **The one flesh bond between us strengthens as we freely interact in ever-deepening ways at all levels of our being: expressing our love by building intimacy.**

This session looks at how we express love to our partner and build intimacy by meeting their emotional needs.

Group Session

Feedback

- Briefly share one insight each of you has gained as a result of the Couple Time following the session about God's purpose and plan for marriage. How has the topic helped you?
- Was there anything in the Introductory Reading for this session about love that prompted you to think about the subject in a new way? Explain.

A Expressing love in our relationship

- What do you think should be distinctive about the way love is expressed within a Christian marriage?

Feeling loved

It's important to understand that we all feel loved in different ways. **We need to understand what makes our partner feel loved, so we can express our love for them** in the way they need it. This requires ***agape* love** (other-centred and unconditional love) which comes from God's Spirit living and active within an individual.

Foundation Principle:
We build intimacy when we express love to our partner in the way they need it.

A Expressing love in our relationship

This is a different kind of Couple Time preparation.
First you will have two to three minutes to write down your answers to i. **Then** you will have five minutes to complete ii and tell each other what you wrote down for i.

i. Jot down your answer to the following question: What does my partner do that makes me feel loved? Write down at least two things.

ii. Then tell each other what you wrote. Make eye contact and say, 'I feel really loved by you when ...'

Note down those things that you do for your partner that they said made them feel loved.

In your Couple Time you will have more time to talk about ways in which you can express love in your marriage.

*'here would be a lot more
ıappy marriages if
ıusbands tried to
ınderstand their wives
and wives tried to
ınderstand football.*

Anon

B Meeting relational needs

We all recognise that we have physical needs such as food and sleep. When these are met we feel satisfied; when not, we may feel irritable. Human beings also have 'relational' needs. Examples of some relational needs are: affection, attention, respect and encouragement. **When our relational needs are met we feel loved and cared for – we experience emotional intimacy.** When they are not met we can feel hurt and unloved. Partners who don't meet each other's emotional needs will likely experience a gradual emotional withdrawal from one another, over time.

David and Deborah

***David** works long hours to provide for his family. On Fridays he likes to go out with his mates to play pool and on Sundays he goes to watch his son play football. In any spare time David likes to do DIY around the house and garden. David is proud of what he has achieved. He* *loves his wife and son and wants them to have everything he didn't when he was growing up. Sometimes he feels guilty about the hours he works. He can't understand why Deborah is often moody and irritable but they don't talk much. Once or twice he has found her crying and he couldn't help feeling annoyed.*

***Deborah** loves being a mum and dotes on her son. It took many years of trying before they had Sam (9) and she has given up hope of having another baby. She is busy in her job at the local school and she does voluntary work with the elderly. She also organises the crèche at church. Deborah has many friends but still feels lonely. She loves her husband but feels she doesn't get much of his time and attention. She also feels that she can't talk to David. Lately she has felt stressed and anxious, that everything is going wrong. She finds herself criticising David the minute he comes home.*

1. Divide into separate groups of men and women to discuss your answers to the following questions. Then, feed back your thoughts to the whole group.

Men consider:

a. What do you think Deborah is feeling?
b. What does Deborah need from David?
c. How can David make Deborah feel more loved and cared for?

Women consider:

a. What do you think David is feeling?
b. What does David need from Deborah?
c. How can Deborah make David feel more loved and cared for?

It's not good to be alone

In the creation account in Genesis, we read that God calls His creation 'very good'. Yet after God creates Adam, suddenly we read that something is 'not good' – the fact that Adam is alone.[4] There is no one suitable for him amongst the animals. God always intended to create a pair of humans but He created them one after the other in order to highlight their need for each other. So God creates Eve to live with and work alongside Adam.

God made us with a need for relationship. Marriage is one of the relationships which God has provided as a remedy for our aloneness. He also made us with a need for a relationship with Him. **We were made to need God *and* need people!**

2. In what ways do we need God? How is it different from needing our partner and other human relationships?

Ten relational needs

The following are ten identified relational needs which, when met, contribute to emotional intimacy (see pages 52–53).[5] These are **specific ways in which *agape* love can become more tangible.** (Note: we sometimes think of 'intimacy' as the physical act alone. While intimacy may include sex it is much more than that. True intimacy is only possible when our relational needs are being met.)

We all have each of these needs to some degree. The intensity and type of our individual needs may vary from time to time. However, for the purpose of this exercise, we are focusing on the relational needs that we most want to have met **at this time** in our lives. Although we **shouldn't** expect our partner to be able to meet every single need we have, **God intends our marriage relationship to be the primary human relationship through which there is giving and receiving to meet these needs.** Giving and receiving is a big part of the process of becoming one in marriage.

3. Do this exercise as a couple:

a. **First,** each couple is allocated two or three (of the ten listed overleaf) relational needs. As a couple think of **a specific action** that illustrates how one partner could meet the need of the other. You may also find it helpful to say what **not** to do.

b. **Then** report back your ideas to the group.

Ten relational needs

I need …		Myself	My partner
Acceptance	Receive me unconditionally; look beyond my faults and irritations, respond positively to me. This means … look beyond the faults and irritations, accepting me as the imperfect person I am, not based on performance. Don't criticise. *'Do you love me just the way I am?'*	☐	☐
Approval	Commend me for who I am. Speak well of me to others. This means … speak highly about aspects of my character, for who I am, to others. Recognise the special things about me. *'Show me that I am special.'*	☐	☐
Affection	Communicate care and closeness through physical touch. Tell me you love me. This means … express your affection by touching me and using loving words. *'I need a cuddle.'*	☐	☐
Appreciation	Verbalise your personal gratefulness for me, notice my achievements. This means … verbally communicate that you are grateful for what I **do.** *'Tell me that you notice me and what I do.'*	☐	☐
Attention	Show interest in and support for my concerns; enter my world with me. This means … listen to me. Spend time with me on my level – no distractions,	☐	☐

I need ...		Myself	My partner
	but give me your undivided attention. *'Come into my world.'*		
Comfort	Share in my pain by feeling the hurt with me, console me with tenderness. This means ... comfort me tenderly when I am hurting. Take my feelings seriously. *'Share in my pain/my struggle.'*	☐	☐
Encouragement	Urge me forward positively; help me persevere towards my goal. This means ... help me to overcome something or work towards a goal, instilling confidence. *'Do you believe in me?'*	☐	☐
Respect	Value my ideas, give regard to my opinions; show me my worth to you. This means ... honour me and don't put me down. *'Show me that I am of great worth to you.'*	☐ X	☐
Security	Protect me from harm, pursue harmony, give me confidence when I am vulnerable. This means ... help me to trust and feel secure when I am vulnerable; create a feeling of freedom from fear or harm (emotional/physical/financial). *'I need to feel safe with you.'*	☐	☐
Support	Come alongside me to gently help me carry a load. This means ... help with a worry or problem. *'I need your help with this.'*	☐	☐

4. By yourself

a. Identify your top three intimacy needs at this point in your life. (Tick three **'myself'** boxes but do not show your partner.)

b. Now guess and note down what you think your partner's top three are at this point in his/her life. (Again don't confer with your partner. Tick three **'My partner'** boxes.)

Couples Together

c. **Are our needs the same?** Compare your top three (the **'Myself'** boxes) to see if any are the same as the **'Myself'** boxes ticked by your partner. For example, both identifying 'security'. Without revealing your specific needs, be ready to tell the group if you had: 3/2/1/0 the same (they don't have to be in the same order).

d. **Do we understand each other?** Compare what you guessed about your partner's top three needs (**'My partner'** boxes ticked) with what he/she actually selected (his/her **'Myself'** boxes ticked). Without revealing specific needs, be ready to tell the group if you guessed: 3/2/1/0 correctly

Foundation Principle:
Meeting the relational needs of our partner is an expression of ***agape*** love and draws us together.

B Meeting relational needs

In your Couple Time be prepared to describe why you selected the particular three relational needs you feel are most important to you at the moment. You will also be talking about how your partner can meet these needs.

C Factors affecting emotional intimacy

Emotional intimacy comes out of a growing awareness of each other's needs. Many people have difficulty recognising or expressing their own needs. If we don't understand or recognise needs – ours or our partner's – it hinders us from giving and receiving appropriately.[6]

Factors affecting the recognition of needs:

Unaware of them	*Just don't understand what our own needs are.*
Uncommunicative	*Don't know how to talk about these things, or feel very uncomfortable doing so.*
Self-reliance	*Believe that all we need to survive and be happy is found within oneself. Those who've experienced a lot of childhood pain may learn to survive by stuffing their feelings inside, and find it difficult to show their true feelings to anyone else.*
Low self-esteem	*Believe we have little worth or reason to be loved. Feel unworthy, unlovable or guilty.*

Steve and Susan

When Susan met Steve she was immediately attracted to his confident and fun-loving personality. They have been married eight years and to the outside world they seem the 'perfect couple'. To his friends Steve is always upbeat and cheerful, never showing any other kinds of feelings. Susan comes from a large family and tries to live up to the high standards set by her mother. Her parents went through a bitter divorce when she was in her teens. Susan doesn't know much about Steve's family except that his father was very strict, and when he died recently Steve hardly said a word about him. Susan feels unloved and frustrated that she can't get close to Steve. She is also worried because she has heard Steve raising his voice several times recently with their five-year-old son, saying things like 'big boys don't cry'. She doesn't know what to do and feels anxious and guilty.

1. Consider Steve and Susan and the factors affecting their emotional intimacy.

a. What might be the reasons that Steve finds it difficult to let Susan get close to him?

b. What might be the reasons that Susan finds it difficult to let Steve get close to her?

c. How might these factors act as barriers to emotional intimacy for Steve and Susan?

d. How does a person handle these factors so that they are better able to meet the needs of their partner?

Foundation Principle:
Together we can learn to handle any barriers to emotional intimacy.

C Factors affecting emotional intimacy

i. As I think about my own needs I relate to the following statement(s): (tick any that apply)

- ☐ I am unaware of my needs.
- ☐ I find it difficult or uncomfortable to communicate my needs.
- ☐ I think it's important to look out for myself first (nobody else will).
- ☐ I find fulfilment from within.
- ☐ 'Big boys and girls' don't cry! All this stuff about needs is rubbish.
- ☐ I feel guilty talking about my needs.
- ☐ Other…

ii. Look at the statements you have ticked above. How might they affect your ability to **receive** expressions of love from your partner? Do any of them act as barriers to building emotional intimacy? (Mark these with a B.)

iii. Which insights from the group discussion could help you be better at **giving** to meet the relational needs of your partner? Note down one or two insights

In your Couple Time you will be able to talk about factors affecting emotional intimacy – your own needs and how you can meet the needs of your partner – so you will be able to give and receive more appropriately.

A special note

As we try to communicate our feelings and needs, we might struggle to let loved ones get close to us or we may become angry in certain situations without knowing why. (We will tackle anger in Session 5.) It can be helpful to talk to a counsellor to unpack these struggles and give an insight into the causes of our behaviour. With this understanding we are much better equipped to change and grow as people. Counselling sometimes has an inappropriate stigma attached to it but there are situations when it is entirely appropriate, particularly if it will help to remove barriers to communication and intimacy. Useful counselling contacts are at: Association of Christian Counsellors 01189 662207 or visit www.acc-uk.org

... And finally

Take a minute to review the Foundation Principles for the session.

Agree on a date for your diaries for your Couple Time:

- 12/1 – [illegible]
- 19/2
- 2/3 – M+S
- 16/3 – [illegible]
- 25/4 – D+S
- 5/5 – [illegible]

Couple Time – 60 minutes

Love conquers all things – except poverty and toothache.

Mae West

As you talk to each other **remember the dos and don'ts of listening.**

A Expressing love in our relationship

If you didn't have time in your group meeting to complete part ii then do it now (page 49).

What one thing could you do for your partner this week that would make them feel loved? Identify a personal action point.

Personal action point:

· Accept, appreciate + attend.
"Not to judge".

B Meeting relational needs

First, affirm your partner by telling them ways that they are already meeting some of your needs (mention at least two things). financial · support the children.

Then, take turns to describe why you selected the three **relational needs** you feel are most important to you at the moment (pages 52–53). Think of ways your partner can meet these needs. Identify a personal action point(s) if appropriate.

Personal action point:

1 of 10 pm listening

C Factors affecting emotional intimacy

Take turns to tell each other which statements for part i you relate to the most as you think about your own relational needs (page 56).
Then talk about how they might act as barriers to building emotional intimacy with your partner (part ii).

What insights from the group discussion could help you be better at giving to meet the relational needs of your partner (part iii)? Does anything need to change in the way you or your partner give and receive love to build emotional intimacy in the future? Identify a personal action point, if necessary.

Personal action point:

Together Notes: 10 Important Relational Needs (on www.togetherinmarriage.com) has more information about relational needs and contact details for 'The Great Commandment Network' and ILM Relational Ministry UK (including training and resources available).

At the next group meeting you will be asked to describe a key insight you've started to apply in expressing love and building emotional intimacy, as a result of the session. Agree on one thing you would be prepared to share with the group from your Couple Time and write it down:

Before the next group meeting ...
Please complete the Introductory Reading for Session 4: **Facing life's relationship challenges with God** (pages 61–63). Relationship challenges and self-centredness can threaten our marriage. We grow closer as we face them with God's help.

NOTES

1. 1 John 4:7–12; John 13:1–13, 34–35.
2. Romans 5:5.
3. 1 John 4:19.
4. Genesis 2:18.
5. Source of teaching on relational needs: Chapter 2, *Keeping Marriages Healthy*, by Dr David and Teresa Ferguson (Intimacy Press, 2000). Adapted and used with permission. For further information on the relational needs, including contact details for 'The Great Commandment Network' and 'ILM Relational Ministry UK' see Together Notes: 10 Important Relational Needs on our website.
6. Adapted from 'The result of unmet need?', Chapter 2, *Keeping Marriages Healthy*, by Dr David and Teresa Ferguson (Intimacy Press, 2000). Used with permission.

4 Facing life's relationship challenges with God

Introductory Reading

Marriage is a special union between two individuals. It is also the closest most of us will ever be to another human and that brings challenges for our relationship.

In the early stages of a relationship we seem to be protected by a romantic glow. There is a high level of physical and emotional intimacy, but as the glow fades we begin to see each other in a different light. **We face a choice: either we ignore any problems or we tackle them together. Choosing the first option will lead us on a path to isolation; the other will draw us closer together.** If we don't want to confront any issues, we risk settling for a rather shallow relationship. In time we are likely to become resentful and bitter, and drift apart. We might still live under the same roof but emotionally we become distant. But it doesn't have to be that way. We can choose to work together, face life's relationship challenges and grow closer in the process.

Relationship challenges

We will look at five areas of challenge to any marriage:[1]

I. **Differences.** It seems obvious: our personalities, gender, family backgrounds, expectations and values are likely to be very different. It is often our differences which attract us to each other, but later on they can drive us up the wall! The situation gets worse when we start focusing on each other's weaknesses.

II. **50:50 performance.** There is a great danger in basing our relationships on performance. In the 50:50 model we each do our bit: I'll meet your needs if you meet mine; if I do this for you then I expect something in return. I may expect my partner to maintain the high standard of performance I will obviously put in. But if I think you're only doing 40% then I'll criticise and cut back to 40% as well.

III. **Tough times.** Our relationship will have to take action to meet life's ups and downs in a constructive way. Naturally we celebrate the highs, but the way we respond to unexpected difficult circumstances can make or break a relationship.

IV. **'Affairs'.** We would define these as any activity where we seek inappropriate fulfilment outside of the marriage. The classic one is the love affair. But many people today have 'career affairs' in which most of their energy is channelled into their work. The 'activities affair' is similar – a hobby or sport can be an all-consuming passion. Love of material things such as shopping, food and so on is another way that we can seek gratification. Children can also take the first place over our relationship with our husband or wife.

Where do I spend my time and money? This is a good indicator of my priorities.

V. **My priorities.** This is the big issue – we all have a natural tendency to put ourselves first. It's the way we are wired: our feelings, needs and happiness come first even if we are not trying to be deliberately selfish. That makes it difficult for the union of two to become a team of one.

I never loved another person the way I loved myself.
Mae West

God has the answer

God can help us face these challenges to our marriage because He helps us to deal with the root of the problem: our self-centred nature.

The world became contaminated by sin when Adam and Eve, the first married couple, chose to go their own way and disobey God.[2] Sin distorts all that is good. **Sin makes people naturally self-centred,[3] which has a catastrophic effect on our relationships with God and with each other.** God seeks an intimate relationship with every person but cannot tolerate sin because He is holy. So we find ourselves separated – disconnected – from Him.

The good news is that God took the initiative to restore a relationship with people – to reconnect. Jesus has dealt with mankind's sin on a cosmic scale through His sacrifice on the cross.[4] **When we turn to Jesus as our Saviour (as one who rescues us) He gives us the Holy Spirit, God's personal presence and power to live in us. We may still live in a challenging world infected by sin, but the Holy Spirit helps us to live God's way, as opposed to our self-centred way.**

'If anyone is thirsty, let him come to me and drink. Whoever believes in me, as the Scripture has said, streams of living water will flow from within him.' By this he meant the Spirit …
John 7:37–39

Who is the Holy Spirit and what does He do?

Jesus promised that God's Holy Spirit would satisfy our deepest longings. **The Holy Spirit is God – the third Person of the Trinity,**[5] **not an 'it'. He is the intimate presence of God in our lives.**[6] **Among the many things the Holy Spirit does are the following:**

- He gives us **new life.**[7]
- He assures us we are a **child of God.**[8]
- He enables us to experience the infinite **love of God.**[9]
- He teaches us **truth.**[10]
- He challenges us about our sin[11] and enables us to **change**[12] – to become other-centred rather than self-centred.
- He helps us **forgive each other.**[13]
- He gives us a **source of love from outside of our marriage** to love one another unconditionally, even when times are tough and we don't feel like it.[14]
- He enables us to **tell others about God.**[15]

If we try to live the Christian life in our own strength we will struggle, because it's impossible! We will experience failure, frustration and lack of fulfilment if we live by our self-centred desires, because they clash with living God's way.[16] We need God's power and guidance to live as He intends and to face our relationship challenges. **For this we must live in step with the Holy Spirit.**

What drives my choices? Is it God's Spirit within me, or my self-centredness?

This session looks at how we can face life's challenges so they don't threaten our relationship, but bring us closer together.

Group Session

Feedback

- What insights or encouragements did you gain from your Couple Time following Session 3 about expressing love?
- Was there anything in the Introductory Reading for this session about relationship challenges and how the Holy Spirit helps us that prompted you to think? Explain.

A Looking at life's relationship challenges

1. How might various kinds of relationship challenges affect a marriage? (Refer to the challenges covered in the Introductory Reading and think of your own ideas. Consider the positive impact as well as the negative.)

Going my own way

We **all** have a natural tendency to put our thoughts, feelings and desires first, before anyone else's interests. This inner bent towards self-centredness is easier to spot in others than in ourselves. Over time, selfishness in a relationship can lead to people drifting apart and eventually feeling isolated.[17]

2. How might it affect a marriage if one or both partners are feeling isolated?

3. Why do you think that some people are willing to tolerate isolation instead of working to build harmony and closeness?

To err is human … to blame it on someone else is management potential.
Anon

Foundation Principle:
Life's relationship challenges may threaten a marriage and lead towards isolation, if we handle them in a self-centred way.

A Looking at life's relationship challenges

Think about the relationship challenges outlined in the Introductory Reading and those you have discussed as a group.

i. How has my relationship been affected by any, or all, of them? Rate how each has affected you, by putting a cross on the line.

Challenges	**How does this affect our marriage?**		
	Negative effect	Not affected	Positive effect
Our differences			
50:50 Performance			
Tough times			
'Affairs'			
Selfishness			
Other ..Priorities			

In your Couple Time be prepared to talk about your answers and in what specific way you think your marriage is affected (positive or negative).

B Facing relationship challenges with God

Bible study

1. Selfishness is rooted in our sinful nature. Dealing with self-centred tendencies is a lifelong process.

a. **First,** each couple is allocated one of the following passages. Read it together and write down your answers to the following:

- Identify a key principle for dealing with sin in our lives.
- How can this principle help build a solid relationship between a husband and wife? Think of a specific example relating to marriage.

b. **Then** report back your ideas to the group. Note down important principles and their application to marriage in the table.

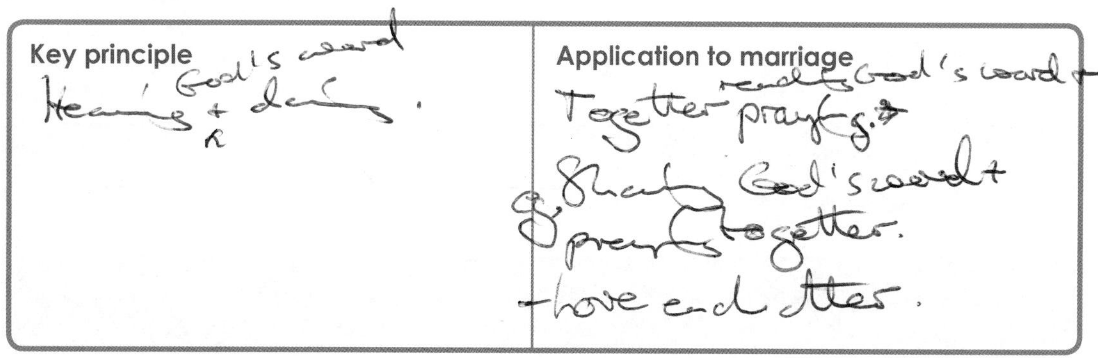

Key principle	Application to marriage

This is the message we heard from Jesus and now declare to you: God is light, and there is no darkness in him at all. So we are lying if we say we have fellowship with God but go on living in spiritual darkness; we are not practicing the truth. But if we are living in the light, as God is in the light, then we have fellowship with each other, and the blood of Jesus, his Son, cleanses us from all sin.
If we claim we have no sin, we are only fooling ourselves and not living in the truth. But if we confess our sins to him, he is faithful and just to forgive us our sins and to cleanse us from all wickedness.
1 John 1:5–9 (NLT)

Therefore, I urge you, brothers, in view of God's mercy, to offer your bodies as living sacrifices, holy and pleasing to God – this is your spiritual act of worship. Do not conform any longer to the pattern of this world, but be transformed by the renewing of your mind. Then you will be able to test and approve what God's will is – his good, pleasing and perfect will.
Romans 12:1–2

If you have any encouragement from being united with Christ, if any comfort from his love, if any fellowship with the Spirit, if any tenderness and compassion, then make my joy complete by being like-minded, having the same love, being one in spirit and purpose. Do nothing out of selfish ambition or vain conceit, but in humility consider others better than yourselves. Each of you should look not only to your own interests, but also to the interests of others.
Philippians 2:1–4

Therefore everyone who hears these words of mine and puts them into practice is like a wise man who built his house on the rock. The rain came down, the streams rose, and the winds blew and beat against that house; yet it did not fall, because it had its foundation on the rock. But everyone who hears these words of mine and does not put them into practice is like a foolish man who built his house on sand. The rain came down, the streams rose, and the winds blew and beat against that house, and it fell with a great crash.
Matthew 7:24–27

And I will ask the Father, and he will give you another Counsellor to be with you for ever – the Spirit of truth. The world cannot accept him, because it neither sees him nor knows him. But you know him, for he lives with you and will be in you.
John 14:16–17

But I tell you the truth: It is for your good that I am going away. Unless I go away, the Counsellor will not come to you; but if I go, I will send him to you. When he comes, he will convict the world of guilt in regard to sin and righteousness and judgment …
John 16:7–8

Foundation Principle:
As we surrender every area of our lives to God, His Word and His Spirit, He will help us face life's relationship challenges and build a stronger marriage.

B Facing relationship challenges with God

i. Note any insights or encouragements from the Bible study feedback that you would like to share with your partner ...

· importance of r+p.

ii. In what way(s), if any, have I been going my own way and been self-centred in our marriage?

· listen
· acknowledge
· love.

In your Couple Time be prepared to talk about building a stronger marriage and dealing with any selfishness.

C Spirit-filled living

1. Why might a husband and wife still have self-centred attitudes or behave in selfish ways, even though they are Christians?

A Spirit-filled life

Jesus came so we can have life to the full by experiencing intimacy with God.[18] But many who express faith in God are not actually experiencing this intimacy because their lives are self-centred rather than God-centred. These Christians have the Holy Spirit – the Spirit of Christ – living in them, but this is not being shown in their attitudes or actions. The Bible refers to them as 'worldly'.[19] **To experience intimacy with God we need to stay close to Him – to be rooted in Christ – in every aspect of our lives, including our marriages, and be filled with His empowering Spirit.** The Bible tells us that God *pours His love into our hearts by the Holy Spirit.*[20] The Bible refers to this kind of person as 'spiritual'.[21]

The worldly Christian		The spiritual Christian	
	• self-centred • in a relationship with God but following self instead of the promptings of the Holy Spirit • living according to personal priorities rather than God's • driven by own strength • lack of spiritual growth • feeling discord and frustration • finds loving others in a Christlike way difficult		• Christ-centred and Spirit-filled • living in step with God's Holy Spirit • motivated to please God resulting in growing harmony with God's purpose • living in God's power • experiences and demonstrates increasing: love, joy, peace, patience, kindness, goodness, faithfulness, gentleness and self-control • shows love for other people in a Christlike way

2. How does an intimate relationship with God enable us to experience intimacy with one another?

3. What gets in the way of our intimacy with God, and one another? What is the remedy?

Spiritual 'breathing'

We all make choices every day – being conscious of the big decisions but not giving a second thought to those smaller daily choices in our attitudes and actions. **It's often in the little things that we sin – choosing to go our own way rather than God's:** watching TV rather than talking to an anxious spouse, staying late at work rather than coming home to give support with demanding toddlers, and so on.

A simple analogy to help us understand how to live a Spirit-filled life is breathing. Breathing air is part of physical day-to-day living. **Spiritual breathing, to keep on being *filled with the Spirit*[22] should be part of daily living as a Christian.** The apostle Paul puts it like this:

I pray that out of his glorious riches he may strengthen you with power through his Spirit in your inner being, so that Christ may dwell in your hearts through faith. And I pray that you, being rooted and established in love, may have power, together with all the saints, to grasp how wide and long and high and deep is the love of Christ, and to know this love that surpasses knowledge – that you may be filled to the measure of all the fulness of God.
Ephesians 3:16–19

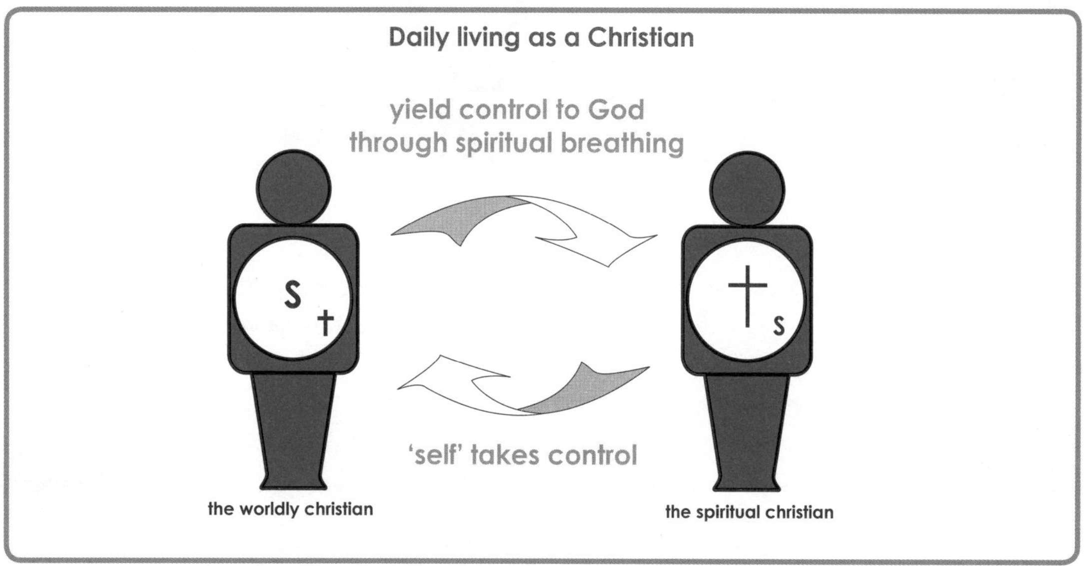

Breathe out **We exhale the 'impure air'.** When we go our own way rather than God's we need to deal with it as soon as we become aware of it (confession). **We need to admit our failures and turn away from our sin (repenting) and back to God.**
KEY VERSE: 1John 1:9

Breathe in **We inhale the 'good air'. We reclaim His forgiveness**[23] **and ask to be filled again with the Holy Spirit.** In surrendering control of our lives again to Christ, we trust the Spirit to fill us again with His presence and power. The verb form 'be filled'[24] implies continuous action. We are to 'keep on being filled' because our dependence on Him needs to be moment by moment – like the 'oxygen of life'.[25]
KEY VERSE: Ephesians 5:18

4. In what practical ways could God's Spirit filling a life make a difference in the marriage?

Foundation Principle:
By living as Spirit-filled people we will increasingly experience intimacy with God and each other.

C Spirit-filled living

i. Is there an area of my marriage where I particularly need to yield to God's Spirit and depend on His power? (Look back at what you wrote down in the Couple Time preparation box **B ii** on page 68 and write down any specific details).

In your Couple Time be prepared to talk about which area you especially want to yield to the Holy Spirit's control.

… And finally

Take a minute to review the Foundation Principles for the session.

Agree on a date for your diaries for your Couple Time:

Couple Time – 60 minutes

> *Nothing takes the taste out of peanut butter quite like unrequited love.*
>
> Charlie Brown

Complete the following individual preparation before you spend time as a couple

Spend 5–10 minutes alone to reflect on the following questions before talking with your partner:

- Do I want the best for my partner and my marriage?
- Do I want to be a Spirit-filled marriage partner?
- Is there an attitude or behaviour I need to confess to God?
- Do I sincerely want to surrender control of my whole life to the Holy Spirit?

Then spend some time in personal prayer (use this suggested prayer if you wish).

Lord Jesus, I'm sorry for ... Thank You for Your forgiveness and cleansing. Help me to live in dependence upon Your Spirit. I want to surrender my selfish desires and allow You to make me the marriage partner You want me to be. Please fill me with Your Spirit. Amen.

Note: The Holy Spirit enters our life when we entrust it to Jesus. While we only need invite Jesus to come into our life once, we will need to ask the Holy Spirit to fill us many times, as we become aware that again we have taken over the control of our life.

Read Knowing God (page 154) if you're not sure about your relationship with God. For more on living in the Spirit read **Together Notes: Living the Christian Life** (visit www.togetherinmarriage.com).

Complete together

As you talk to each other **remember the dos and don'ts of listening.**

A Looking at life's relationship challenges

Take turns describing how you feel the various challenges have affected your marriage (page 65). Is there anything you could do to protect your marriage against anything that threatens (or might threaten) your relationship?

Identify a personal action point, if required.

Personal action point:

listen to God / Sylvia ....

B Facing relationship challenges with God

Share your insights or encouragements from the discussion in answer to i (page 68). Then share your answers to ii. **Note:** this question is not intended to prompt accusations of selfishness in your partner. Instead focus on ways **you** might have been self-centred.

In what ways can you deal with any self-centredness to build a stronger marriage? (If you wish, go on to **C. Spirit-filled living** to help you.) Identify a personal action point, if required.

Personal action point:

C Spirit-filled living

Take turns telling each other in which areas of your marriage, if any, you feel you need to yield to God's Spirit and depend on His power (page 71). Identify a personal action point, if necessary.

Why not practise 'spiritual breathing' together by praying, either silently or out loud.

Personal action point:

Spiritual focus for our marriage – Hold back? Yield –
– home – welcome God.

Not good at / not great supporting each other's weakness.

There are optional additional questions for remarried couples overleaf.

For further reading:
Sorted by David Wilson (Agapé, 2000), gives lots of helpful information about getting in step with the Holy Spirit in your Christian life.

At the next group time you will be asked to talk about a new insight you have gained about the Holy Spirit and how He is helping you in your marriage. Agree on one thing you would be prepared to share with the group from your Couple Time and write it down:

Before the next group meeting …
Please complete the Introductory Reading for Session 5: **Handling our feelings constructively** (pages 77–79). The way we handle feelings can drive us apart or we can grow closer as we learn to understand and accept the feelings of our partner.

For remarried couples

(optional additional questions)

i. Do you need to ask the Holy Spirit to heal you or your partner of hurts from the past which have not fully healed, or, if healed, wounds that are easily reopened due to being in a new marriage?

ii. Agree on one thing you could do to support your partner as you face these challenges together.

NOTES

1. Adapted from 'Five Threats to Oneness', *FamilyLife USA Weekend to Remember* conference manual (Revised January 2004). Used with permission.
2. Genesis 3.
3. Romans 3:23.
4. John 3:16.
5. The 'Trinity' is a word for God mysteriously revealing Himself as the three Persons of the Godhead (Father–Son–Spirit) unified as one. The Bible does not use the word 'Trinity', but Father–Son–Spirit are used together in the context of being equally God, eg Matthew 28:19; John 14:6–31.
6. Ephesians 2:18; John 14:16–17.
7. John 3:3–8.
8. Romans 8:15–16.
9. Romans 5:5; Ephesians 3:18–19.
10. John 14:17; John 15:26; John 16:13–15.
11. John 16:5–8.
12. Romans 8:1–17; Colossians 3.
13. Ephesians 4:32; Colossians 3:13.
14. Galatians 5:22–25; Romans 5:5; 1 John 4:7–8.
15. John 15:26–27; Acts 1:8.
16. Galatians 3:3; 5:17.
17. Adapted from *Going Your Own Way* and questions 5 and 6 of *Building Your Marriage* (Group Publishing, copyright © Dennis Rainey, 2000). Used with permission.
18. John 10:9–11.
19. 1 Corinthians 2:14–3:3.
20. Romans 5:5.
21. 1 Corinthians 2:14–3:3.
22. Ephesians 5:18.
23. 1 John 1:9
24. Ephesians 5:18.
25. David Wilson, 'Provision for life', *Sorted* (Agapé, 2000).

5 Handling our feelings constructively

Introductory Reading

Human beings are wired to feel and express a huge range of emotions, both positive and negative. Positive feelings, like love and joy, obviously help to grow a strong marriage. But negative and painful feelings can completely overwhelm us and make us behave in ways that can damage us as well as our relationships, unless we learn to handle them constructively. This session looks at handling anger and the emotions that lie underneath it.

Learning to recognise 'negative' emotions

Some emotions are easy to spot, whereas others are not so easy to recognise. Intense angry feelings are obvious like the 'tip of the iceberg'. Less obvious are milder forms of anger such as annoyance, irritation or frustration. Anger, in whatever form, is triggered by other more painful feelings that lie 'below the waterline', and it's these emotions that are usually more difficult to recognise. **Experts refer to feelings like anger as the *secondary* emotions and the deeper feelings as primary emotions.**

Primary emotions are strong feelings like insecurity, disappointment, worry, guilt, jealousy, rejection and fear. For example, Kevin and Katherine are arguing about cancelling their holiday. Katherine is angry and Kevin is irritable. But neither is expressing the primary emotion underneath. For Katherine the primary emotion is fear: she's exhausted and fearful of what will happen if she doesn't get a break, so doesn't want to cancel it. For Kevin it is worry: he might miss out on a promotion if he doesn't cancel the holiday.

What lies underneath my anger; irritation or frustration?

Unless a person admits their anger and identifies the primary underlying emotion(s) they will be unable to deal with the root cause and really grow in the relationship. But **if a person is able to learn to recognise the feelings underlying their anger, then they will be better able to identify the root cause and come up with a constructive solution.**

How people express their emotions

People express their emotions in different ways, depending partly on temperament and partly on patterns picked up from the past. Most of us tend to fall into one of two groups:[1]

I. **'Exploders': express emotions openly.** They spew out what's inside, easily blowing up in irritation, frustration or aggression (*'I'm sick and tired of your ...'*). Some unleash their anger by shouting. A few may even express emotions by lashing out physically. If such aggression gets out of control it can lead to violence and abuse. **Unless exploders learn to manage their emotions they will not only hurt others but also themselves, because they often frighten away the very people to whom they want to get close**.

II. **'Stuffers' don't express emotions openly.** They stuff or bottle up their feelings, internalising them. Some deny or try to ignore their feelings in order to avoid uncomfortable situations (*'I don't want to talk about it!'*). They may withdraw into their shell or even leave in order to protect themselves from being hurt. Some hide behind activities or children. They might display prickly behaviour, or make sarcastic or cutting remarks. Others express their emotions in subtle ways: Frank expressed his aggression subtly by overspending and Fiona expressed hers by making Frank cucumber sandwiches, which she knew he hated! **Stuffers hurt others because they are not open with their feelings, making it difficult to know and relate to the real person.** But they also hurt themselves because suppressed anger or other negative or painful feelings can lead to bitterness, resentment, ulcers, high blood pressure and even depression.

How do I express anger? How does it affect my partner?

Effects of strong emotions

Strong emotions affect the person feeling them AND the person on the receiving end, the partner. They tend to cloud judgment so we are not able to make wise decisions when affected by them. We also tend to see situations from our own point of view. This means **we can have very negative interpretations of our partner's actions.**[2] For example, Peter returns home from work and asks, *'What's for dinner?'* He gets angry because *he thinks* Pam doesn't show him enough love and respect when she only heats up frozen pizza instead of preparing a more substantial meal. Pam works just as long hours as Peter and *she thinks* she is doing him a favour by preparing food at all. She gets defensive and angry too. Both see the issue of dinner through their own eyes, and feel unappreciated by the other.

Do we need to talk?

God doesn't say that we shouldn't feel angry (He gave us the emotion in the first place!). But, He doesn't want us to let negative emotions turn into bitterness, rage or bad behaviour.[3] **He does say we should handle it in the right way. Anger can be positive, as a signal that something is wrong and requires action.** We should deal with anger quickly and get to the bottom of the issue so it doesn't smoulder. Otherwise the devil can fan it into a flame of hatred, pride, self-pity or self-righteousness.[4] This requires good communication at a level of trust and openness. We should find ways of expressing our feelings constructively.[5] And we need to listen to one another in a way that seeks to understand the root causes of the anger (the primary emotions) and accept them. This can be hard.

A fool gives full vent to his anger, but a wise man keeps himself under control.
Proverbs 29:11

God understands anger

God was angry when mankind rejected Him and His directions for life, but He chose not to pour out His anger on us. Out of His great love for us He sacrificed His Son, resulting in peace between us and Himself.[6]

While our anger is more often petty and selfish, unlike the holy and righteous anger of God, we can still learn from this example. If we ask Him, He will help us make the sacrifice of putting aside our desire to retaliate, and learn to deal with our own anger and that expressed by our partner.

This session looks at how we can handle our emotions to develop a closer relationship.

Group Session

Feedback

- What insights or encouragements did you gain from your Couple Time following the session on facing challenges with the Holy Spirit (page 73)?
- Was there anything in the Introductory Reading for this session about handling our feelings that prompted you to think about the subject in a new way? Explain.

A special note

It is not possible to cover all aspects of handling feelings in this session, so we will focus on anger and how to handle it in a way that will strengthen a marriage.

A Understanding Anger

When talking about anger we should realise that there are different forms of anger. At the 'tip of the iceberg' are intense angry feelings. But there are lesser forms of anger which are milder feelings, such as annoyance, irritation or frustration. When we use the word 'anger' in this study it includes all the milder feelings too.

To understand anger better there are two things we need to know: firstly, what makes us angry, and secondly, how our anger is expressed.

I. **What makes us angry?** No one can make us angry – we are each responsible for our own feelings and how we handle them. **Anger is triggered by primary emotions, which are other more painful feelings that lie deeper.** These are not always recognised, so they are shown as 'below the waterline' in the diagram. The secondary emotions are shown as 'above the waterline' because they are easy to see.

II. **How is our anger expressed?** Put simply, some people express anger openly ('exploders'), but others internalise or 'bottle up' their feelings ('stuffers').

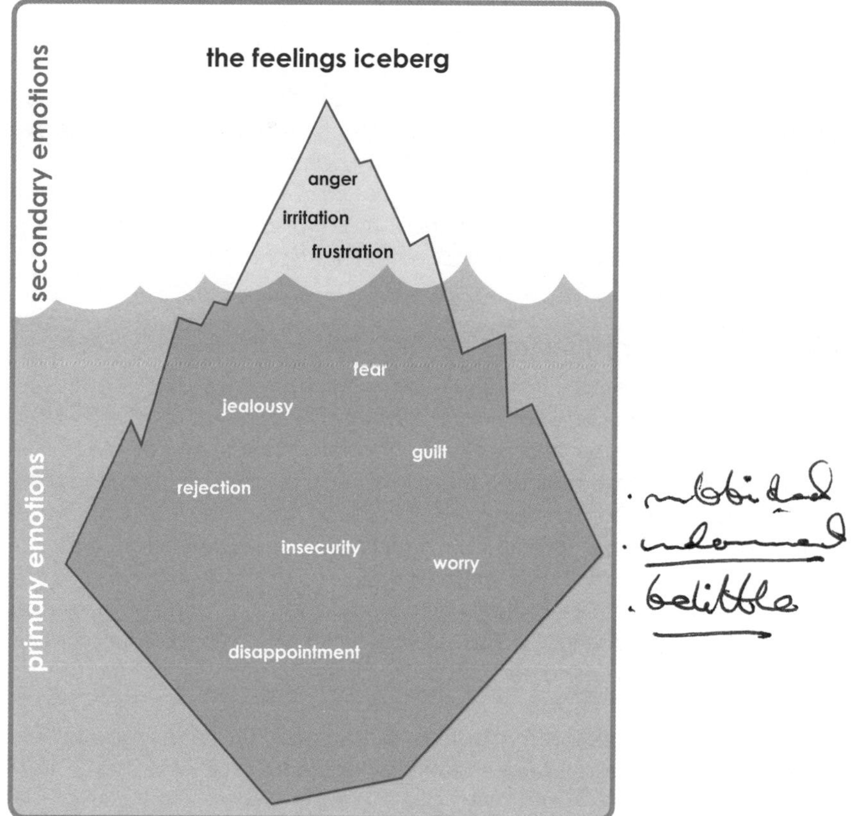

Unaddressed anger can damage relationships and drive us apart. On the positive side, anger can be a signal to take action which will help build a closer relationship. A healthy start is to admit to ourselves what we are really feeling (both the anger and the primary emotion underneath).

Edward and Esther

At a party, Esther sees Edward paying a lot of attention to a woman considerably younger and more attractive than she is. Later, when he returns to her, she asks sharply, 'What's the matter, Romeo? Did Juliet throw you off her balcony?'

1. What primary emotion(s) prompted Esther's reaction? In what way(s) is she expressing her feelings? How could she handle her feelings better?

George and Gina

George returns home late from work, exhausted. The porch light isn't working and he struggles to get his key in the lock to open the front door. He finds Gina at the kitchen table, engrossed in paperwork. George notices the bank statements and his credit card bill lying amongst the scattered papers. From the look on Gina's face he suspects that he has exceeded his credit limit again. Gina looks up and says, 'I think we're going to have to forget ideas of going on that cruise. I don't think we can afford it.' George, now exploding, grabs the papers and shouts, 'I told you there was nothing to worry about … I'm getting my credit limit increased.' Gina gets up, her face reddening, saying, 'I'm going to bed. Your dinner is in the oven.' Then she slams the door behind her.

2. What primary emotion(s) might have prompted George's reaction? In what way(s) is he expressing his feelings? How could he handle his feelings better?

   What primary emotion(s) might have prompted Gina's reaction? In what way(s) is she expressing her feelings? How could she handle her feelings better?

3. Controlling anger can often be difficult. Why do you think this is? Why is bottling up anger not a healthy solution?

Foundation Principle:
Anger is a signal that something is not right and that the underlying feelings need to be addressed.

A Understanding anger

Write down answers to the following four questions:

i. In what situation(s) do I tend to get angry or irritated or frustrated with my partner? (Note down any typical scenarios, including those where there is no strong expression of angry feelings or anger is internalised.)

• tired – want's undivided attention.
: " – want's to do something 'bored' but nothing constructive
– wants more than I can provide – material ...

ii. What are the likely primary emotions? (Tick what might be underneath my anger.)

- □ Insecurity □ tiredness
- □ Disappointment
- □ Guilt
- □ Jealousy
- □ Fear
- □ Rejection
- □ Injustice ('It's not fair ...')
- ☑ Other ...

– not providing for my wife / family.

iii. How do I typically react when I'm angry with my partner? (Tick any in the table that apply.)

iv. How do I typically react when my partner is angry with me? (Tick any that apply.)

Reactions	How do I react when **I am** angry/irritated/frustrated	How do I react when **my partner is** angry/irritated/frustrated
• Blow up in a rage	□	□
• Get depressed	□	□
• Get physical	□	□
• Cry	□	□
• Run away	□	□
• Suppress it with silence	□	□
• Making cutting or sarcastic remarks	□	□
• Humour or teasing	□	□
• Other ...	□	□

In your Couple Time be prepared to talk about your answers and what you can do to help each other to understand each other's anger in a constructive way.

f we take martrimony at its owest, we regard it as a sort of friendship recognised by he police.
Robert Louis Stevenson

B God's help for anger management

Genuine happiness is when a wife sees a double chin on her husband's old girl friend.
Anon

Bible study

Therefore each of you must put off falsehood and speak truthfully to his neighbour, for we are all members of one body. 'In your anger do not sin': Do not let the sun go down while you are still angry, and do not give the devil a foothold …

Get rid of all bitterness, rage and anger, brawling and slander, along with every form of malice. Be kind and compassionate to one another, forgiving each other, just as in Christ God forgave you.
Ephesians 4:25–27,31–32

1. What insights does the passage give about anger? You might want to consider:

- Is anger always wrong? When does anger become sin?
- What do you think it means to not 'let the sun go down while you are still angry'?
- How does God want us to handle anger?

Ps: 78

God's way of dealing with anger

God was angry when mankind rejected Him and His holy ways.[7] This anger was dealt with on a cosmic scale by His Son,[8] who chose to take God's wrath upon Himself as an act of love when He submitted to being sacrificed on the cross. From this we can learn that **sacrifice and self-control are needed in handling anger.**

The three suitcases in the diagram opposite show different ways people can handle anger.

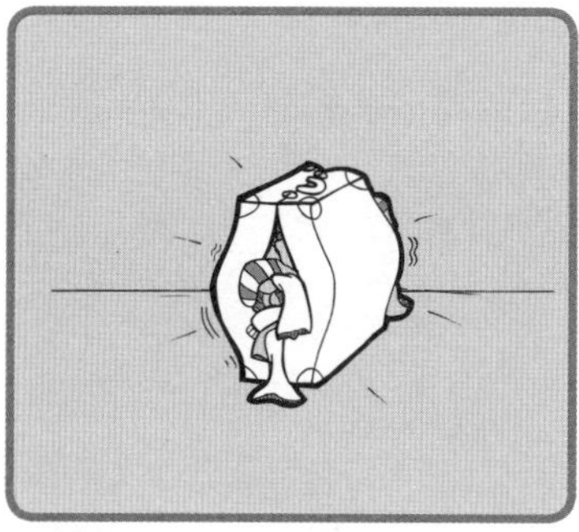

CASE 1: keeping our anger locked inside

CASE 2: letting our anger explode

CASE 3: taking anger to God in prayer. We do this by:

- **giving God our feelings and asking Him to show us what lies beneath** – the primary emotions and the reasons why we are feeling the way we do.
- **asking Jesus to show us what to do.**
- **sacrificing the desire to retaliate and choosing to love instead,** leaving judgment to God.
- **'breathing spiritually'** – confessing any wrong attitudes and hurt we may have caused. Asking God to fill us afresh with His Spirit. Asking for peace and the power of self-control to express our feelings constructively.

If we are on the receiving end of anger expressed by our partner, we can do this by:

- **asking God to help us with our feelings** (as per bullets above).
- **asking God to give us the strength not to retaliate and to accept the feelings of our partner,** whether we are the cause or not, as an expression of our love.
- **asking God to help us forgive or be forgiven.**

2. How might it help you handle **your own** anger if you took it to God? How might it help you if you typically:

- keep anger locked inside?
- let anger explode?

3. How might it help you handle **your partner's** anger if you took it to God?

Foundation Principle:
God helps us to deal with the anger of others and to control our own.

- Stuffer
  - more peace
  - less retaliation
  - less bitterness
  - less fear of withdrawing from partner.
- exploder
  - self-control
  - less rage
  - retaliation without hurt

It's practically impossible to look at a penguin and feel angry.

Joe Moor

B God's help with anger management

How do I want to see my relationship with God help me to:

i. handle my own anger/irritation/frustration? (Tick any in the table that apply.)

ii. handle the feelings of my partner? (Tick any in the table that apply.)

God's help	How do I want God to help me handle **my feelings?**	How do I want God to help me handle **my partner's feelings**
• Look at guidelines from His Word in the Bible on how to handle anger.	☐	☐
• Enable me to understand how I express my anger at the moment.	☐	☐
• Show me the underlying primary emotion so I can deal with the root cause.	☐	☐
• Give me the strength and self-control to handle my own feelings.	☐	☐
• Give me the courage to accept the feelings of my partner.	☑	☐
• Help me accept anger because of the sacrifice made by Jesus.	☐	☐
• Help me sacrifice my desire to retaliate when my partner has hurt me.	☑	☐
• Fill me with His peace.	☐	☐
• Convict me of inappropriate ways I deal with anger.	☐	☐
• Other …	☐	☐

In your Couple Time be prepared to talk about how God can help you handle anger personally and as a couple.

C Handling anger constructively

God wants us to handle anger with self-control. We start by treating the anger as a signal to take action and take our feelings to God. **The next step is to tell our partner what we are feeling – not by attacking him or her with angry words but by expressing our feelings constructively, by 'speaking the truth in love'.**[9] This takes deeper levels of communication (Session 1). We discuss what lies underneath the anger to identify the root cause and take action to address it. By doing this we expand our understanding of each other and grow closer together.

Expressing negative feelings constructively

It is possible to speak honestly yet avoid accusing your partner, by using 'I' messages instead of 'you' messages.

X 'you' messages	✓ 'I' messages
• Attack the partner's faults • Are directed towards your partner • Express judgment of the other	• Reflect personal emotions • Are directed towards oneself • Express individual feelings

1. Look at the example of an 'I'/'you' message and then rewrite the following 'you' messages into constructive 'I' messages:

Example
'You' message– *'Your driving is going to get us all killed!'*
'I' message – *'I feel very frightened and worried by your driving.'*

a. *'It's typical of you to roll over and go to sleep like nothing has happened.'*

b. *'You don't think of anyone but yourself. At these events you're always going off and talking to everyone except me.'*

c. *'That's just like you to spend so much money on something we don't really need.'*

d. *'Why don't you ever listen to me?'*

Foundation Principle:
Handle anger by expressing your feelings constructively.

Listening actively to understand

The next step is taken by our partners. They should listen actively to understand the feelings being expressed. **Active listening means giving your full attention to the one speaking and is an expression of other-centred love.** It is helpful for the listener to repeat in their own words what is being said ('reflect back') to check that they have understood. The listener should also ask clarifying questions if they are unsure of what the speaker is trying to say.

The goal of the listening partner is to understand and accept the feelings being communicated.

2. How do you feel when someone has really listened to you? Good. Positive

3. Look at the following example and then work out what you could say to reflect back what has been said below to show you have been actively listening.

Example of 'I' message and good reflecting back.

Complete this

I feel a little rejected when you spend ages talking to your friends on the phone and then don't seem to want to sit and talk with me.

So you're saying that you feel a little rejected, like you don't matter to me, when I am on the phone so much ... ?

a.

I'm tired and frustrated that I seem to be the one doing more than my fair share of the housework.

So you're tired and frustrated with doing more than your fair share of the housework.

b.

I'm hurt that you come home so late regularly. I feel insecure and worry that you're really out having a good time without me.

So you feel insecure and worry when I come home late that I'm having a good time without you

Foundation Principle:
Understand your partner's feelings by listening actively.

C Handling anger constructively

Think about any recent 'anger situations'. Remember these may involve milder feelings of irritation or frustration, rather than overt anger.

i. In what ways do I handle angry feelings (mine or my partner's) well?

• listen/understand reflect give attention/respect.
• discuss at a good time, – [illegible]

ii. In what ways can I be more constructive?

•

In your Couple Time be prepared to actively listen to each other and find ways of handling anger more constructively, if necessary.

… And finally

Take a minute to review the Foundation Principles for the session.

Agree on a date for your diaries for your Couple Time:

10/3 – chez M&S.

16/3 – [illegible] + Martin

20/4 – [illegible]

5/5. –

Couple Time – 60 minutes

When angry, count ten before you speak; if very angry, a hundred.
Thomas Jefferson

Note: Anger can be a very sensitive subject for many people, whether they experience intense angry feelings or only mild irritation or frustration. **Pick a good time to have your Couple Time** (preferably not when you are very tired). It can be helpful to pray before you start. Be gentle and sensitive towards each other as you talk about your feelings. We all grow up with different experiences of handling anger and sometimes those experiences run very deep. **Make a point of affirming your love and acceptance for your partner** whatever feelings they express, and try to understand them more fully through this discussion.

A Understanding anger

First, talk about your own anger. Take turns to describe the situation(s) that tend to make you feel angry (refer to your notes on page 81). Talk about how you react and why you react the way you do – what are the primary emotions you are feeling? What are you managing well? Does anything need to change?

Then, talk about how you react to angry feelings expressed by your partner. Identify a personal action point, if required.

Personal action point:

Visit our website and take a few minutes to look at Together Notes: Managing Anger together which has much more on how to handle anger positively.

B God's help with anger management

Talk about how God helps or could help you handle your anger, or anger expressed by your partner (see page 87 and the notes on page 85). Identify a personal action point, if required.

Personal action point:

C Handling anger constructively

First, take turns to tell each other in what ways you handle feelings well (yours or your partner's) and how you could handle them more constructively (if necessary).

Then, take turns to describe a recent example of an 'anger situation' using an 'I' message whilst your partner listens actively. Does anything need to change in the way you or your partner handle situations in the future? Identify a personal action point, if appropriate.

Personal action point:

- listen + support

For further reading:
The Other Side of Love by Gary Chapman (Moody Publishers, 1999) is filled with insights and techniques to help understand the source of anger and guide you towards a productive outcome.

At the next group meeting you will be asked to describe a key insight you've started to apply in handling feelings constructively with your partner as a result of the session. Agree on one thing you would be prepared to share with the group from your Couple Time and write it down:

Before the next group meeting …
Please complete the Introductory Reading for Session 6: **Living positively with our differences** (pages 95–97). Our differences can divide us through conflict. But, we grow closer when we handle them in a godly way. We can also grow as people.

For remarried couples

(optional additional questions)

Note: You or your partner – or both of you – may have experienced a bereavement or divorce. In both cases there are likely to be strong emotions associated with the past and it is vital for both partners to deal with these appropriately. This is not about restoring a relationship with a divorced partner, but about handling resulting emotions so you are free to move on and build a strong and healthy new marriage. For bereaved partners there may still be issues from the past, which are hurting your current marriage.[10]

Take some time to reflect and then talk together. Be gentle. It is a good idea to pray first and ask God for wisdom and sensitivity.

i. What do you feel when you think about **your** relationship with your former partner? Or, what do you feel when you think about **your partner's** relationship with his/her former partner?

   Are you struggling with anything?

ii. Agree on one thing you could do to support your partner as you face any challenges together.

NOTES

1. Adapted from 'Resolving Conflict: Communication III – understanding the anatomy of anger', *FamilyLife USA Weekend to Remember* conference manual, revised 1.04. Used with permission.
2. Matthew 7:1–5.
3. Ephesians 4:31.
4. Ephesians 4:25–27.
5. Ephesians 4:29.
6. It is worth remembering two important points concerning God's wrath and the death of Jesus: God did not take out His anger on people (although they deserved it). Instead, He took His wrath upon Himself in the Person of Jesus. Secondly, the Bible makes it clear that Jesus willingly sacrificed Himself: Matthew 26:39; Mark 14:36; Luke 22:42.
7. Psalm 78.
8. 1 Thessalonians 5:9–10.
9. Ephesians 4:15.
10. Adapted from 'Session 4: HomeBuilders Project' Question 3, *Making Your Remarriage Last* (Group Publishing, copyright © Jim Keller 2001). Used with permission.

6 Living positively with our differences

Introductory Reading

Opposites attract ... but that 'perfect match' may end up being a dual rather than a duet. **As a married couple, we need to learn to live with the differences we each bring into the relationship** – backgrounds, personalities and needs, as well as thoughts, feelings and ways of seeing the world. Then we have to navigate our way through work schedules, household responsibilities, and differing opinions on money, sex, friends, in-laws and, possibly, children. The very things that first attracted us to each other and brought spice to our relationship can often end up causing frustration and arguments.

Marriage is the world's most expensive way of discovering your own faults.
Anon

Making our differences work

We don't just have to 'grin and bear it' – we can learn to make our differences work for the good.

Our differences add richness to our relationship and can strengthen a marriage. When we appreciate our differences and work together – to complement one another – we will be stronger together than when apart. Also, God can use our differences as tools for personal growth, knocking off some sharp edges. **In marriage we will have our weaknesses exposed. We can learn to embrace the strengths of our partner into our own lives. As we compromise, we change and grow as people.** We will have the opportunity to try new ideas, new activities, make new friends, learn to take a few more risks or learn to take more care. This growing process can be uncomfortable, even painful, but as we step out of our own comfort zone we will develop greater personal 'wholeness' and grow a closer relationship ... if we handle the inevitable conflicts well.

In what ways are we different? Do those differences annoy me or challenge me to develop personally?

The conflict zone

Handling conflicts well means understanding the different stages which can lead to a spiral of ongoing conflict.[1]

I. **Conflict starts when there is a clash of our differences** – an initial offence that causes hurt. This offence could be quite trivial (forgetting to put the top on the toothpaste, cutting it fine to get to the station, a look or tone of voice) or more serious (money, sex, children). It may have been done unknowingly, or it may be deliberate. Of course, **underlying any conflict is our native selfishness – our tendency to want things to go our own way**.

II. **The initial offence causes hurt, and that hurt may produce irritation, frustration or anger.** Some people choose to fight ('exploders') and others to withdraw ('stuffers'). At this point, the person who has felt the hurt has a choice: to decide to bring up the issue so that both can work together to resolve it; or to ignore the hurt, leaving a seemingly small issue unresolved. Meanwhile the other partner may not even be aware that he/she has caused hurt.

III. **One unresolved hurt is often followed by another** (small things can accumulate) and may result in overreacting to something else. This can lead to retaliation by the other person and the spiral goes round again, with a build up of hurt, anger and further 'offences'.

IV. **We stop the conflict spiral when we decide to stop ignoring the issue or trying to get our own way (or get even), and make a conscious decision to resolve the matter.**

Am I out to change the way my partner is or to resolve the issue and grow our relationship? Am I prepared to recognise that my behaviour may be part of the problem?

Resources for resolving conflict

The first requirement is an unselfish attitude. Good communication is also important, as is the way we handle anger. God tells us to 'speak the truth in love'.[2] We might be able to speak out, but forget to be loving ('exploders'). Some of us are loving, but unable to face our partner and speak truthfully, if the truth is painful ('stuffers'). **Perhaps the most loving thing we can do when we have a difficult conversation is to listen.**

Rodney, have I done something to upset you?

Listening and talking through issues will often provide an acceptable solution. **But if we want to restore our relationship and feel connected again, we need to forgive. Forgiveness means 'letting go' of the offence, whether it's serious or trivial.** It is not a feeling, but a decision. When the person who has been hurt chooses to forgive, they let go of resentment. When the partner who has caused the hurt receives forgiveness, they are free to love again. Our ability to forgive the one who has hurt us, and to ask for forgiveness if we have caused the hurt, are both linked to our relationship to God.[3]

To forgive is to set the prisoner free … only to discover the prisoner was you.

Anon

How do I feel about God's forgiveness of me?

God forgives us and helps us to forgive others

God has shown us grace: even though we didn't deserve it, He has extended His unconditional love and pardon to us through Jesus.[4] We can respond by receiving His forgiveness as a gift and enjoy living as people who have been forgiven. God gives us the power to forgive one another through His Spirit (Session 4). When we experience this in a deep way, we will be able to more easily forgive others.

It's worth noting that when we forgive, we do not automatically forget. We need an ongoing process of healing and reconciliation to rebuild trust and closeness with our partners.

This session looks at how we can resolve our differences so they don't divide us through conflict, but bring us closer together.

Group Session

Feedback

- What insights or encouragements did you gain from your Couple Time following the session on handling our feelings constructively?
- Was there anything in the Introductory Reading for this session about living with our differences that prompted you to think about the subject in a new way? Explain.

A Understanding and handling our differences

Opposites often attract each other. But even if we're not complete opposites we all have different ways of looking at life, likes and dislikes. Our differences can often result in disagreement and ongoing conflict. **The Bible tells us that a clash of differences between people can be constructive.**

As iron sharpens iron, so one man sharpens another.
Proverbs 27:17

1. In what ways can the principle of 'iron sharpening iron' benefit a marriage?

Foundation Principle:
Our differences can be tools that help us grow as people and grow stronger in our marriage.

A Understanding and handling differences

i. Note down one or two insights from the group discussion that you would like to share with your partner.

ii. Identify one important difference between you and your partner, eg

• money:	spend it/save it
• sport:	budding athlete/couch potato
• holidays:	seek adventure/rest
• temperament:	'glass half full'/'half empty'
• lifestyle:	spontaneous/make plans and stick to them
• people:	spend time with others/prefer to spend time alone
• focus:	relationships/task more important
• approach to tasks	big picture/detail
• other…	

In your Couple Time be prepared to talk about how you could use this difference as a catalyst for personal change and growth in your marriage.

… A psychiatrist asks a lot of expensive questions your wife asks for nothing.

Joey Adams

B Handling conflict

In marriage we are forced to live with our differences and some of them will lead to conflict, whether we like it or not. Whatever the reasons for our conflicts, if we leave them unresolved we will be likely to find ourselves drifting apart. But if we learn to resolve them well, we will experience even greater closeness with each other.

John and Jenni – conflicting priorities

John is a spontaneous people person and is very focused in his work. Jenni is sensitive, emotional and likes to plan carefully. It's late and Jenni is in bed, reading. John comes home and joins her in the bedroom.

Jenni: *(with frustration)* You're late, what happened?

John: *(in an upbeat tone)* Hello, darling! I did say on the phone this afternoon that I would be home late.

Jenni: *(extremely irritated)* It's nearly eleven o'clock! I got the impression from your call that you'd be home for dinner. I waited until 8.30pm. I even tried to call you on your mobile, but it was switched off!

John: *(soothingly)* Sorry, Jen. Mr Lewis arrived unannounced and invited the whole team out for drinks. I couldn't say no. And I couldn't get a signal on my mobile.

Jenni: *(incredulous, in a loud voice)* You couldn't say no!?!

John: Jenni, you know how important this contract is.

Jenni: *(trying hard to be calm)* I feel really hurt. I made a nice meal so we could spend some time together. I feel let down. You said you'd be home.

John: I'm sorry, darling, what can I say? Look, it's late and I'm tired ...

Jenni: You always say that. You work late nearly every night and when you don't, you're out with people from the office! You're always putting your work first – I think you love your work more than me!

John: *(a little defensively)* Please don't start with all that again. I am trying hard to keep everyone happy. I'm under a lot of pressure right now. We have to pay the bills ... you know how tight the money situation is! Look, Jen, I need to do this and I need you to bear with me. It's my big chance. It will be better next month.

John hugs Jenni and leaves the room quickly.

Jenni: *(in an exasperated tone)* You said that last month ... *(even more quietly)* ... and the month before.

1. In what ways are John and Jenni handling their conflict well? Not so well?
   Note: This question is not about judging who is right or wrong.

2. What else could John do? Jenni do?

Marriage is an alliance entered into by a man who can't sleep with the window shut, and a woman who can't sleep with the window open.

George Bernard Shaw

Foundation Principle:
Loving confrontation is the first step towards resolving conflict.

Learning about forgiveness

A simple sincere apology is an important part of resolving conflict. Admitting and acknowledging our part in the disagreement means we are taking responsibility for any hurt we have caused. But saying sorry is usually not enough. We need to take another step to admit we were wrong and ask our partner's forgiveness. And the offended partner needs to let go of the hurt by forgiving the person who has caused it. Forgiveness is vital in order to let go of the BIG HURTS, but it's also really important when dealing with those daily trivial things that upset us.

Bible study

21 Then Peter came to Jesus and asked, 'Lord, how many times shall I forgive my brother
when he sins against me? Up to seven times?'
22 Jesus answered, 'I tell you, not seven times, but seventy-seven times.
23 'Therefore, the kingdom of heaven is like a king who wanted to settle accounts with his
servants. 24 As he began the settlement, a man who owed him ten thousand talents[a] was
brought to him. 25 Since he was not able to pay, the master ordered that he and his wife and
his children and all that he had be sold to repay the debt.
26 'The servant fell on his knees before him. "Be patient with me," he begged, "and I will pay
back everything." 27 The servant's master took pity on him, cancelled the debt and let him go.
28 'But when that servant went out, he found one of his fellow-servants who owed him a
hundred denarii.[b] He grabbed him and began to choke him. "Pay back what you owe
me!" he demanded.
29 'His fellow-servant fell to his knees and begged him, "Be patient with me, and I will pay
you back."
30 'But he refused. Instead, he went off and had the man thrown into prison until he could
pay the debt. 31 When the other servants saw what had happened, they were greatly
distressed and went and told their master everything that had happened.
32 'Then the master called the servant in. "You wicked servant," he said, "I cancelled all
that debt of yours because you begged me to. 33 Shouldn't you have had mercy on your
fellow-servant just as I had on you?" 34 In anger his master turned him over to the jailers to be
tortured, until he should pay back all he owed.
35 'This is how my heavenly Father will treat each of you unless you forgive your brother from
your heart.'
Matthew 18:21–35

NOTES FROM PASSAGE

a. A talent was equivalent to fifteen years of income.
b. A denarius was a coin worth the equivalent of a day's wages.

3. What do we learn from the passage about forgiveness? You might want to consider:

- What effect should the king's forgiveness of the debt have had on the servant?
- What were the consequences of refusing to forgive?

4. How does experiencing God's forgiveness in our own lives help us to forgive others?

Forgiveness in marriage

Conflict is rarely about one person being right and the other wrong. It's usually about two different people with different expectations and needs. **To resolve an issue each person should take responsibility for their own part in the situation**.

- The one who has been hurt should acknowledge their feelings.
- The one who has caused the hurt needs to ask for forgiveness.
- The one who has been hurt should offer forgiveness.
- Forgiveness needs to be accepted.
- If both sides have caused hurt (as is often the case), then they both need to forgive one another and forgiveness will flow both ways to restore the relationship.

Forgiving does not mean pretending that nothing has happened, or forgetting there is a wound. **Forgiving does not condone a wrong action. Forgiving is a conscious act and requires strength.** It is the first stage in an ongoing process of healing and is an essential step in resolving conflict. **Forgiving sets free the person who caused the hurt as well as the one who offers forgiveness.**

5. Why is it sometimes difficult to forgive? What are the consequences of refusing to forgive in marriage? (Note: consider the 'little' things as well as the big ones.)

Foundation Principle:
Forgiving one another is the second step towards resolving conflict.

... not forgiving is like drinking rat poison and waiting for the rat to die.
Anne Lamott

B Handling conflict

i. What are the ways I tend to react and handle conflict in my marriage? (Tick any that apply. REALITY CHECK: would my partner agree with my assessment?)

- ☐ talk calmly and try to work things out
- ☐ withdraw from conflict
- ☐ get defensive and argue
- ☐ get very heated verbally
- ☐ get physical
- ☐ freeze up, with no reaction
- ☐ deny or struggle to fully acknowledge being hurt
- ☐ find it difficult to explain how I feel
- ☐ find it difficult to listen and understand
- ☐ find it difficult to genuinely apologise
- ☐ find it hard to accept *my partner's* view
- ☐ find it hard to accept that *my* behaviour may be part of the problem
- ☐ other ...

ii. Think about the following statements and how they express your thoughts and feelings. Where do I generally see myself regarding this issue? (Put your initials somewhere on the line to indicate.)

iii. Where do I think my partner generally is regarding these issues? (Put your partner's initials on the line, as appropriate.)

	almost never	**sometimes**	**often**
I am able to say when I have been hurt by my partner.			
I am able to admit what I have done to hurt my partner.			
I am able to apologise.			
I rely on God to help me with forgiveness.			
I am able to forgive my partner even when I feel hurt.			
When I have forgiven I don't hold any grudges.			
In forgiving, I am able to show my partner love.			

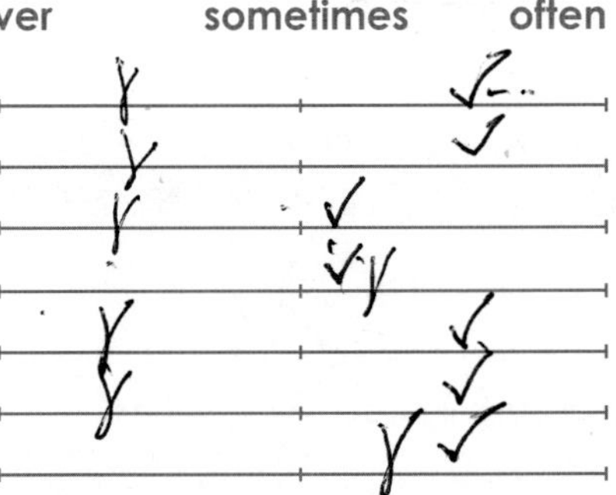

In your Couple Time be prepared to talk to your partner about how you perceive you handle conflict – what goes well and not so well. Also, explain why you placed the initials where you did for part ii.

C Finding full reconciliation and building closeness

When we experience conflict, saying sorry and expressing forgiveness to one another are not enough. We need to be reconciled – to grow together again, and rebuild trust.

1. In the process of conflict resolution, how do we:

- Restore closeness?
- Rebuild trust?

2. How can we live with a less than ideal situation? (A neat and tidy resolution is not always possible.)

Foundation Principle:
The third step to resolving conflict is to agree on actions that bring reconciliation and restore closeness.

C Finding full reconciliation and building closeness

i. Note down one or two insights from the group discussion about finding full reconciliation that you would like to share with your partner …

In your Couple Time be prepared to talk as a couple about reconciliation and building closeness after a conflict.

… And finally

Take a minute to review the Foundation Principles for the session.

Agree on a date in your diaries for your Couple Time:

A good marriage is the union of two good forgivers.
Ruth Bell Graham

Couple Time – 60 minutes

Note: Talking about conflict when you're **not** having a disagreement is very important. It allows you to think and talk calmly about how you handle your differences. Make sure you pick a good situation to have your Couple Time. We all grow up with different experiences of handling conflict. Make a point of seeking to understand each other and to **be positive** as you talk.

A Understanding and handling differences

First, share your insights from the group discussion about how differences between marriage partners can be positive.

Then tell each other what difference you selected for part ii (page 99). How can you use this as a growth point for personal change? How can it be a growth point in your marriage? Identify an action point, if appropriate.

Personal action point:
Be creative -

Look at Together Notes: Three Steps for Resolving Conflict on our website for more on the steps for resolving conflict well.

B Handling conflict

Talk about how you tend to react in conflict situations (refer to your notes for i on page 103). Why is this the case? Does anything need to change? Identify a personal action point, if necessary.

Then, explain why you placed the initials for yourself and your partner where you did for part ii. In what areas are you doing well? Are there areas that need to change? Identify a personal action point to enable you to manage the process of forgiveness better, if necessary.

Personal action point:
• admit / acknowledge

C Finding full reconciliation and building closeness

Talk about your insights from the group discussion to help you move towards greater reconciliation and closeness after a conflict (refer to your notes on page 104). Do you need to agree on a specific step to help you in the process of reconciliation? Agree an action point, if appropriate.

Personal action point:

· Apologise specifically + clearly.

For further reading:
Fighting for Your Marriage, Markman, Stanley & Blumberg (San Francisco: Jossey-Bass, 2001). Includes exercises to help you make changes in the way you handle conflict.

At the next group meeting you will be asked to describe one aspect of resolving conflicts that you've agreed to do differently in the future with your partner as a result of the session. Agree on one thing you would be prepared to share with the group from your Couple Time and write it down:

Before the next group meeting …
Please complete the Introductory Reading for Session 7: **Deepening our physical and spiritual intimacy** (pages 109–111). Physical and spiritual intimacies are part of God's plan for two becoming 'one flesh'. As we deepen these aspects of our intimacy we will grow closer together.

For remarried couples

(optional additional questions)

These questions are not about restoring a relationship with a divorced partner, but about issues of forgiveness so you are free to move on and build a strong and healthy new marriage.

Take some time to reflect and then talk together. Be gentle. It is a good idea to pray first and ask God for wisdom and sensitivity.

i. Do you need to forgive your former partner for anything, or, if applicable, your partner's ex-wife or ex-husband? Is there anything you need to forgive yourself for? Does there need to be a loving confrontation with anyone on any issue?

ii. Agree on one thing you could do to support your partner as you face these challenges together.

For couples with children

(optional additional questions)

i. Think about how you handle your emotions and any conflict in front of your children. What do you think they see – what are you modelling to them?

ii. Does anything need to change to help your children learn to handle conflict and emotions well? Identify an action point, if appropriate.

NOTES

1. Excerpt taken from Dr Gary and Barbara Rosberg's book *Healing the Hurt in Your Marriage*, a Focus on the Family book. Copyright © 2004, Gary and Barbara Rosberg. All rights reserved. International copyright secured. Used by permission.
2. Ephesians 4:15.
3. Ephesians 4:32.
4. John 3:16–17; Romans 8:1–2; 2 Corinthians 5:19; Ephesians 1:7; Colossians 2:13; Hebrews 10:14.

7 Deepening our physical and spiritual intimacy

Introductory Reading

As human beings we crave love, in the form of a deep and intimate relationship. Marriage is one of God's answers to our need. We develop love and intimacy in a marriage as we feel free to share all of ourselves: emotionally, physically and spiritually. We have already looked at how to build emotional intimacy through open and trusting communication (Session 1) and meeting each other's relational needs (Session 3). This session covers two other forms of intimacy.

ow free do I feel to share all f myself with my partner?

Physical intimacy

Western culture is dominated by sex, but often cheapens it. The Church has frequently presented unhelpful views on sex, but the Bible is clear that we are physical beings, 'fearfully and wonderfully made'.[1] God designed male and female bodies to fit together perfectly, as 'one flesh'. There is nothing shameful in this. **God invented sex and meant it to be good: for bonding,[2] pleasure[3] and reproduction.[4]**

We express our deep commitment and love for one another through a faithful and loving sexual relationship. It is interesting that humans are the only creatures whose physical union is face-to-face.[5] The Bible advises that we should only abstain from sex by agreement for a specific period for the purpose of prayer and fasting. Then we should come together again so that neither partner is tempted to stray outside of the marriage.[6] **The Bible says that the marriage bed is for mutual satisfaction and that we should give ourselves to our partner to meet their needs.[7]**

A healthy relationship

Many couples enjoy healthy sex lives, but for others it can be an aspect of their marriage with which they struggle. Some may even feel that they are failing in some way. Lots of couples would like to have a more satisfying physical relationship but don't know how to make it better. **A satisfying sex life is like the icing on the cake … but we have to bake the cake first!**[8] There is no single formula to develop a fulfilling sex life because every couple is different, but there are some key issues we could consider:

I. **Men and women tend to have very different needs.** Generally speaking, for a woman intercourse is linked to the quality of the relationship. She wants to feel valued and cared for. Deep and fulfilling physical intimacy grows out of meeting each other's emotional, relational needs (Session 3). Women also need time to be wooed.

Most men can isolate sex from the other parts of the marriage and are quickly aroused and ready for action. Men may also subconsciously use sex as a way to release built-up fears, joys, tensions and excitement[9] and are hoping that their wives will be as sexually interested as they are.[10]

II. **We need to communicate our needs, likes and dislikes in the sexual area.** We might find this uncomfortable, but unless we talk about these things we will never know what our partner really wants or likes. God intends us to be 'naked and without shame'.[11] When we talk we should be honest, but also kind; respecting each other's feelings and insecurities.

III. **Resolve to work on things that get in the way:** tiredness and stress, a lack of privacy, communication problems, unresolved anger, a problem that needs forgiving, loss of trust, anxiety, too much TV … to name a few!

IV. **Avoid dangerous traps!** There are a few things we should avoid if we want to enjoy a healthy sex life. We shouldn't spend regular periods of time alone with members of the opposite sex. This may be a slippery slope to an affair. We should also be cautious about which films and other media we consume because they can give us unrealistic expectations about sex and make our partner feel inadequate. Some people believe that pornography can spice up a flagging sex life, but this is untrue. Pornographic images have a way of entering our imaginations, bringing another 'person' into our marriage bed. Also porn is like a drug in that we end up looking for stronger stuff to get aroused. Someone usually ends up getting hurt.

There is a deep emotional and spiritual connection when we make love, so it is important to nurture our physical relationship through all the seasons of life.

For a woman, sexual intercourse is the culmination of her responses to tenderness, sacrificial love and even spiritual leadership from her husband.

Roger and Donna Vann
Secrets of a Growing Marriage

What do I like about our sex life

A husband doesn't want a body to perform on, he wants a person who will respond to him in the physical terms that are so meaningful to him … Without it, a husband loses a sense of his masculine self esteem …

Lewis and Hendrick
Rocking the Roles

Rodney wasn't sure how to tell Mabel that he'd had something else in mind when he suggested an early night

Spiritual intimacy

A marriage connects us at a spiritual level, whether we are aware of it or not, because we are spiritual beings. Spiritual intimacy is more than reading the Bible, praying or doing 'churchy' things together, although those things contribute to it. **Spiritual intimacy means connecting at a deep level, drawing close to God together as our heartfelt desire and submitting to His will for our lives.**[12] Then we can draw on His love and leadership and harness His power in our marriages.

The problem is we are in different places spiritually ...

Why is spiritual intimacy important?

I feel uncomfortable sharing my spiritual side with my partner ...

I. **God gives us a solid foundation.** We can't really know ourselves until we know God. As our Creator, He gives us a firm foundation for our lives: identity as His children;[13] security in His promises and significance and purpose for living.[14] If we try to build the foundations of our lives on other things, such as work, money, status, power, education, material things, or even on the love of our partner, then we will be let down. **God is eternal, powerful and loving. If we build the foundations of our lives on a shared relationship with Him, we will build a much stronger marriage.**

II. **God is love and He is its source.**[15] He promises to pour Himself into our hearts through His Spirit so we can love each other with His *agape* love:[16] other-centred, unconditional, seeking the greatest good. **Only the love of Christ can truly bind a marriage together and bless it.** Other kinds of love are self-centred and will tend to pull us apart rather than draw us together.

The secret of life is finding relationship with God. The richer your relationship with God, the richer your relationship with your partner.
Selwyn Hughes, *Marriage God's Way*

III. **God makes our marriage stronger.**[17] He blesses relationships in which either or both partners are trusting in Him.[18] He will shape us as individuals and marriage partners as we seek His will and power for growth and change.

This session looks at how we can grow closer as we deepen our physical and spiritual intimacy.

Group Session

Feedback

- What insights or encouragements did you gain from your Couple Time following the session on living positively with our differences?
- Was there anything in the Introductory Reading for this session about our physical and spiritual intimacy that prompted you to think about the subject in a new way? Explain.

A Deepening physical intimacy

Physical intimacy and sex are expressions of our 'one flesh' relationship and enhance our sense of emotional intimacy (Session 3). **Deep and fulfilling physical intimacy grows out of meeting each other's emotional, relational needs first.** While this session is not intended to be a good sex guide, we will look briefly at what God thinks of sex.

It must be admitted that we English have sex on the brain, which is a very unfortunate place to have it.
Malcolm Muggeridge

1. What is society's view of physical intimacy?

Bible study

2. Read the following passages from the Bible.

- Summarise what you think is the general principle from each as it relates to sex in marriage.
- How should these principles shape our attitude to our own sex life as partners?

If a man has recently married, he must not be sent to war or have any other duty laid on him. For one year he is to be free to stay at home and bring happiness to the wife he has married.
Deuteronomy 24:5

May your fountain be blessed, and may you rejoice in the wife of your youth. A loving doe, a graceful deer – may her breasts satisfy you always, may you ever be captivated by her love.
Proverbs 5:18–19

[2]But since there is so much immorality, each man should have his own wife, and each
woman her own husband. [3]The husband should fulfil his marital duty to his wife, and likewise
the wife to her husband. [4]The wife's body does not belong to her alone but also to her
husband. In the same way, the husband's body does not belong to him alone but also to his
wife. [5]Do not deprive each other except by mutual consent and for a time, so that you may
devote yourselves to prayer. Then come together again so that Satan will not tempt you
because of your lack of self-control.
1 Corinthians 7:2–5

[9]You've captured my heart, dear friend. You looked at me, and I fell in love. One look my
way and I was hopelessly in love! [10]How beautiful your love, dear, dear friend – far more
pleasing than a fine, rare wine, your fragrance more exotic than select spices. [11]The kisses of
your lips are honey, my love, every syllable you speak a delicacy to savor. Your clothes smell
like the wild outdoors, the ozone scent of high mountains.
Song of Songs 4:9–11 (The Message)

The body is not meant for sexual immorality, but for the Lord, and the Lord for the body. [14]By
his power God raised the Lord from the dead, and he will raise us also. [15]Do you not know
that your bodies are members of Christ himself? Shall I then take the members of Christ and
unite them with a prostitute? Never! [16]Do you not know that he who unites himself with a
prostitute is one with her in body? For it is said, "The two will become one flesh." [17]But he who
unites himself with the Lord is one with him in spirit.
[18]Flee from sexual immorality. All other sins a man commits are outside his body, but he who
sins sexually sins against his own body. [19]Do you not know that your body is a temple of the
Holy Spirit, who is in you, whom you have received from God? You are not your own; [20]you
were bought at a price. Therefore honour God with your body.
1 Corinthians 6:13b–20

Foundation Principle:
God is pro sex in marriage.

A Deepening physical intimacy

i. One thing I like about our sex life now is …

• intimacy / closeness –

ii. What elements of our sex life would I like to discuss with my partner to build greater physical intimacy?

- ☐ Positive anticipation
- ☐ Romantic atmosphere
- ☐ Seduction
- ☐ Tender words
- ☐ Non-sexual touching
- ☐ More time for lovemaking
- ☐ Initiating lovemaking
- ☐ Greater variety
- ☐ Deeper responsiveness
- ☐ Clearing the air about a concern
- ☐ Other … [illegible]

In your Couple Time be prepared to talk about your sex life and how you might meet each other's needs. You are encouraged to look together at Together Notes: Differences in Sexuality Between Men and Women, which contains information about the differences in sexuality between men and women, as well as questions to help you talk about sex.

Despite the claims of some sex manuals, a couple cannot separate sex from the rest of the marriage, perfecting it and then isolating it, as it were, in an airtight compartment to be used when desired. Everything that happens in a marriage has its effect on the lovemaking experience.

Ed Wheat, M.D.
and Gaye Wheat
Intended for Pleasure

B Developing spiritual intimacy

Intimacy is the freedom to share all of yourself with your partner. Two persons are 'becoming one' in three distinct dimensions:

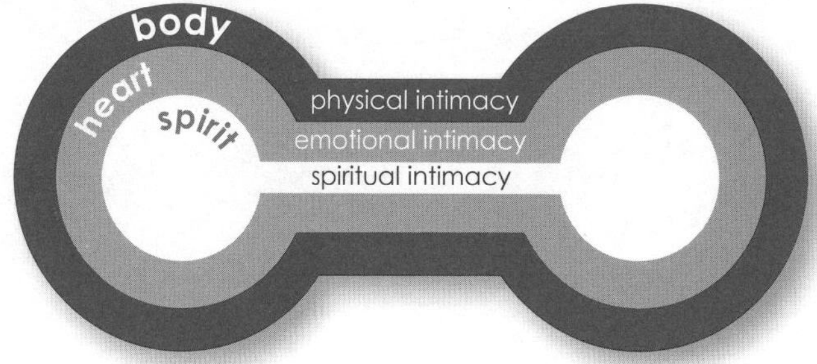

Our bodies become intimate through physical expressions of love: touching, hugging, kissing and sex. We share our hearts through open and trusting communication (Session 1) and meeting each other's emotional needs (Session 3). At the deepest level there is a spiritual connection between marriage partners.

1. What are the effects on a marriage if

- both partners share a living faith and relationship with Jesus?
- one partner has a living faith and relationship with Jesus, and the other does not?
- neither of the partners has a living faith in Jesus?

2. Spiritual intimacy comes as we seek the will of God for our lives together. What are some ways that a couple can develop spiritual intimacy in a marriage?

Foundation Principle:
Spiritual unity needs to be expressed in tangible ways.

B Developing spiritual intimacy

i. How can I support my partner in his/her own spiritual development?

ii. What part could any of the following play in developing your spiritual intimacy? (Tick any you want to discuss or write down your own idea.)

- ☐ Developing my individual relationship with Jesus
- ☐ Reading and discussing the Bible together
- ☐ Praying aloud together
- ☐ Attending church together
- ☐ Working together to help others in need
- ☐ Deciding together to give financially
- ☐ My idea ...

In your Couple Time be prepared to talk about developing the spiritual intimacy in your marriage.

C Deepening our spiritual intimacy

We all have different experiences of prayer. Many people only know 'prayers before bed' and 'grace' at meal times. Some people take part in formal set prayers in church and others pray openly in all kinds of settings. Many people feel comfortable praying in private and find the idea of praying out loud difficult and uncomfortable. Whatever our experiences and feelings about prayer, it is an essential part of drawing close to God.

1. Many married Christians tend to only pray alone and/or in church groups. Few pray as couples. Why do you think this is? Is praying aloud together a personal option or an essential part of growing together in a Christian marriage?

2. What advice or guidelines might help a couple move forward in praying aloud together?

Foundation Principle:
Praying together deepens spiritual intimacy.

C Deepening our spiritual intimacy

i. How do I feel about praying aloud together? (Tick any that apply.)

- ☐ Excited
- ☑ Quite comfortable
- ☐ Uncomfortable
- ☐ Embarrassed
- ☐ Terrified!
- ☐ Open to trying it
- ☐ Other …

ii. Write down any insights from the group discussion, or ideas of your own, which could help you move forward in your prayer life as a couple.

In your Couple Time be prepared to talk about praying together as a couple.

… And finally

Take a minute to review the Foundation Principles for the session.

Agree on a date in your diaries for your Couple Time:

Note:
The Introductory Reading for Session 8 is longer to enable us to explore this complex issue of how God intends us to fit together based on biblical principles.

The only people who make love all the time are liars.
Louis Jordan

Couple Time – 60 minutes

Note: Many couples find it very difficult to talk about sex. Be gentle and patient with one another. Affirm one another. Don't criticise. Remember that deep and fulfilling physical intimacy grows out of meeting each other's emotional, relational needs **first**.

A Deepening physical intimacy

Firstly tell each other what you like about your sex life at the moment.

Talk about the elements of your sex life you ticked during the group session (page 114) and why you selected them.

Identify one thing **you** could do **for your partner** to build greater physical intimacy, if appropriate.

Personal action point:

Take time.

Visit our website and look at Together Notes: Differences in Sexuality Between Men and Women for questions to help you talk about sex.

B Developing spiritual intimacy

Take turns in sharing your answers to part i (page 115). Then tell your partner what you ticked for part ii (if anything) and elaborate on why you ticked it. If developing your spiritual intimacy together is important in your marriage right now, agree what you could do together. Identify an action point, if appropriate.

Personal action point:

Pray more.
Pray for our children/family/friends etc

For further reading:

Rob Bell, *Sex God* (Zondervan, 2007). Fantastic insight into our sexual and spiritual connections.

Barrie and Eileen Jones, *When2Pray* (RoperPenberthy Publishing, 2003). Full of practical and helpful insights to help you pray together as a couple.

www.cwr.org.uk
There are a variety of devotionals available to help you study the Bible regularly.

C Deepening our spiritual intimacy

Talk about what you wrote concerning your feelings about praying aloud together and how you could move forward in this area of prayer (page 116). Identify a personal action point, if appropriate.

Why not pray together now … If you are not used to praying together, here are some tips:

- You might begin simply by each praying one sentence about a particular topic, before moving on to the next topic.
- Try to avoid having one person pray a long prayer, which then leaves the other feeling that there is nothing to say!
- Take turns and think of it as including God in your conversation.
- Periods of silence are OK.

Personal action point:

Note:
Praying together builds spiritual unity. We can express our gratitude to God together. We can pray for our general concerns and specific problems. We can pray for, and thereby support, each other in our work, home life, marriage, wider family issues and children. As we express our thoughts and feelings together before God, we let His power and love into our lives. Our thoughts, attitudes and love for one another will change and grow, and so will our intimacy.

At the next group meeting you will be asked to describe one way you are starting to express love differently towards your partner as a result of the session. Agree on one thing each of you would be prepared to share briefly with the group from your Couple Time and write it down:

Before the next group meeting …
Please complete the Introductory Reading for Session 8: **Fitting together as husbands and wives** (pages 121–125). This session looks at how we can grow closer when we live together, in a way that complements one another. Remember to give yourself a few more minutes to read as it's slightly longer than other sessions. It will set up your group meeting – and maybe blow away some preconceived ideas!

Why not sign up to receive weekly e-prayers from when2pray to help you pray together as well as pray for others. Investigate **www.when2pray.net**

NOTES

1. Psalm 139:14.
2. Genesis 2:24.
3. Deuteronomy 24:5; Proverbs 5:18–19; Song of Songs; 1 Corinthians 7:2–5.
4. Genesis 1:28.
5. Source: Ed Wheat M.D. and Gaye Wheat, *Intended for Pleasure*, 3rd Edition (Grand Rapids: Revell, 2002) chapter 1.
6. 1 Corinthians 7:5–6.
7. 1 Corinthians 7:2–5. This passage is often misused to justify sexual 'rights'. The context of this passage is actually about mutual satisfaction and pleasure. The Christian wife is not the property of her husband. Sex is not his right and her obligation. Paul is saying that the husband and wife belong to each other and the marriage bed is a place for meeting each other's sexual needs. The passage is not about 'demanding' or 'taking'. The emphasis is about 'giving' of oneself and of mutual responsibility. Source: Gordon D. Fee, *The New International Commentary on the New Testament, The First Epistle to the Corinthians* (Grand Rapids: Eerdmans Publishing Company, 1987).
8. Roger and Donna Vann, *Secrets of a Growing Marriage* (London: Hodder & Stoughton, 1986).
9. Ibid.
10. Willard Harley, *His Needs, Her Needs* (Oxford: Monarch Books, 1986).
11. Genesis 2:25.
12. Source: 'Developing Spiritual Intimacy in Marriage', an article by Norman Wright. www.familylife.com
13. John 1:12; Ephesians 1:5.
14. Romans 8.
15. 1 John 4:7–8.
16. Romans 5:5.
17. Ecclesiastes 4:9–12.
18. 1 Corinthians 7:14–16.

8 Fitting together as husbands and wives

Introductory Reading

When we marry we change from being two independent people to being a new unit as a couple. But how should this new unit operate? Our culture has enormous influence over our view of how men and women should function within marriage, and the result is often different from what God intended.

Many of us harbour unconscious deep-seated expectations about the roles men and women play in a marriage based on what our parents did. Then, we may either try to be like them or else determine to be as different as possible. We may also have strong views based on certain stereotypes of dominant and subservient roles or we may reject the whole idea of roles altogether. Sadly the Church too has presented roles for men and women which cannot always be biblically supported.

What are the greatest influences on my view of the roles of a husband and a wife: parents, my culture, TV...? What are they telling me?

Sometimes I wonder if men and women really suit each other. Perhaps they should live next door and just visit now and then.
Katherine Hepburn

The trouble is, if we don't find a positive way of 'fitting together' we can end up undermining, manipulating or competing against one another. This will prevent us living effectively together as a united team. This session looks at what the Bible says about how God has designed us to fit together.

God's design: we're made for each other

God did not make humans as isolated units or self-sufficient creatures. **He made us to be in relationship:** two creatures made from the same stuff, yet different, bonded together as one flesh. **In this 'profound mystery'[1] of marriage there is no loss of identity, rather a relationship where the two together are greater than when apart.**

When God created men and women He made them of **equal value – both in the image of God – but clearly not the same.**[2]

God made man from the 'dust'. The man's first task was to name the animals. Perhaps it was while he was naming the animal pairs that he recognised what God had known all along, a need to have his own mate.

God set about making woman from the man's side – to be at his side as a 'suitable helper'[3] because man alone could not fulfil God's purposes. The woman wasn't (and isn't) just there to have babies and make life more pleasant, nor as some kind of inferior sidekick, but as someone to **complement the man through an intimate relationship**.

A wife of noble character who can find? She is worth far more than rubies.
Her husband has full confidence in her and lacks nothing of value. She brings him good, not harm, all the days of her life.
Proverbs 31:10–12

God intends for a husband and wife to live together in marriage as a united team.[4] God blessed the man and the woman and **together** they are told to 'fill' the earth and 'rule' over it on His behalf. We have a joint responsibility to care for the world – accountable to God as His representatives or managers.[5]

Marriage: designed to be a harmonious partnership

In my house I'm the boss, my wife is just the decision-maker.

Woody Allen

The God of the Bible is the God of order, not of chaos. God extends the ordering of human life and relationships into marriage, families and the wider community.[6] He has put a divine harmony into His design for marriage and provided practical instructions to fit together so that each partner gives something of themselves for the good of the other. God gives us each a role in the marriage and with it comes responsibilities.

I. **In His divine design for marriage, God gives the husband a role as 'head'.**

Now I want you to realize that the head of every man is Christ, and the head of the woman is man, and the head of Christ is God.
1 Corinthians 11:3

But it is vital to God's order that Christ is the head of man and God the Father is the head of Christ. Christ is a husband's role model for headship. At the same time, He is the One to whom a husband is accountable. Headship has nothing to do with worth. The word 'head'[7] has a range of meanings: literally as the head which governs a body; a metaphorical meaning for head is as 'source' for life. Head also means a person with final authority, responsibility and accountability.

Being the **head does NOT mean one who lords it over another. Instead the husband is to be the head – like Christ.** Christ is the head of the Church body but also its humble servant,[9] the One who showed us what sacrificial love is like.[10] **A husband as Christlike man is one who serves and loves his wife sacrificially.** He also cherishes and takes care of his wife enabling her to maximise and fulfil her God-given potential.[11]

II. **God gives the wife the role of 'helper' – an equal partner to live and work alongside her husband.**

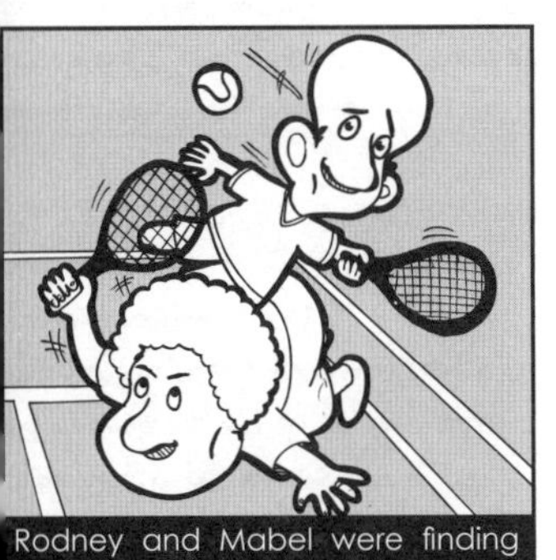

Rodney and Mabel were finding mixed doubles a challenge

The LORD God said, 'It is not good for the man to be alone. I will make a helper suitable for him.' *Genesis 2:18*

The Bible also uses the term 'helper' to describe the help which comes from God.[12] There is **no sense of inferiority at all**, rather it describes one who enables and defends the other. The wife is to be a companion who fits or matches her husband in a way that supports and respects him as his equal.[13]

God's creation design became distorted by sin in Genesis 3. This was the birth of the battle between the sexes, which continues in a world infected by sin. When husbands or wives seek to go their own way, rather than God's, the marriage can end up on a slippery slope where one or both are either seeking to dominate or fight for control, or they are abdicating their responsibilities altogether. But there is hope because Jesus has brought forgiveness and restored our relationship with God and each other.[14] God will help us bring about a harmonious partnership if we are willing to make important choices.

Marriage in real life: important choices

The most important choice we can make to fit together is to allow God to have control of our marriages. This means we each surrender ourselves – submit our individual hearts and wills to God's will.[15] **This isn't a one-off event, but a way of life** that involves daily choices to live God's way – filled with His Spirit – and not according to selfish desires. Yielding control to God doesn't mean that we will instantly become the perfect couple or never argue. It will mean that **God will influence our decisions and behaviour towards one another in a way that will over time strengthen our marriage.** The Bible gives a picture of this kind of marriage as a rope of three cords that is not easily broken, where two of the strands are represented by the husband and wife and the third is God.[16]

Perhaps it was the recognition of the daily struggles in marriage amongst the Ephesians that prompted Paul the apostle to stress some important messages for husbands and wives which are just as relevant today, because they are rooted in God's creation design. The first is for husbands and wives to **'submit to one another out of reverence for Christ'.**[17] When we come into marriage, inevitably we will have to give up some of our own independent desires for the sake of our unity. So **marriage becomes a series of daily small decisions and sacrifices for the sake of the other person:** don't leave clothes on the floor; remember to squeeze the toothpaste from the bottom; take out the rubbish when asked and so on.

My wife is always making little digs or criticising me. Nothing ever pleases her so I've given up trying to do anything.

Paul was also trying to communicate a 'profound mystery', namely that the out-working of the relationship between a husband and wife is meant to illustrate for the world the relationship of Christ to His Church. For the husband, Paul emphasised the need to love his wife as Christ loves the Church – giving himself up for her.[18] For the wife it was to submit to her husband as the Church submits to Christ.[19] **The instructions for husbands and wives are in essence very similar: doing what is best for the other person and the marriage. Putting them first, after God, but before work, children, hobbies ...**

Maybe I would submit to my husband if his behaviour were a little more Christlike. The problem is it isn't! He can be so insensitive to my needs.

The big problem is that in this fallen world, marriage forces us to face up to the sin of wanting our own way.

The first question is: do we wait until our partner 'deserves' our actions or do we take the initiative and behave in the way we know we should, the other-centred way, even though we don't feel like it? It's chicken and egg ... who goes first? **We can freely choose the other-centred way, bearing with the weaknesses and foibles of our partner. Or we can choose the way of our old sinful nature and do what we want or feel like.** Whichever way we choose, we will reap what we sow. One way leads to gradual isolation, the other to growing oneness.

There was only one chocolate left. The question was, who was going to crack first?

The next question is: **Which kind of behaviour is more likely to lead to oneness in the marriage?** Manipulation, constant disrespectful behaviour, acts of domination or bullying may all lead to abdication of responsibility within our God-given roles, and withdrawal. However, an atmosphere of unconditional love and initiating other-centred behaviour will motivate your partner towards Christlike love and actions.

Husbands and wives make important choices every day about the way they live together. Those daily choices 'form a delicate and beautiful dynamic that cannot be pinned down with rules'.[20] **We can't change another person, but we can change ourselves. If we ask God to fill us with a spirit of humility, we will find we can do things according to His will, and not the way we would naturally tend.**

OK, so who cleans the floors and who brings home the bacon?

The Bible is silent on who should cook and clean. Different cultures have different expectations of who does what and how. **A woman's sole role is not necessarily only about having children and looking after the home**, although this is a wonderful, fulfilling and demanding job. The 'wife of noble character' from Proverbs 31 is more like 'wonder-woman': capable and hardworking as a successful business woman, wise and respected in the community, caring for the poor as well as running a home.

How do we manage our time and money? How do we honour God as we fulfil our responsibilities together; in the home, at work, or in the community?

Similarly **a man is not expected to earn all the money**, although the Bible does say that he has a responsibility to provide for the needs of his family.[21] A loving husband would want to do his fair share in the home and play an active role in bringing up any children. Again and again Proverbs reminds fathers of their responsibilities in raising children. It's worth remembering too that Jesus loved and valued children. Jesus also cooked fish for His disciples!

A husband and wife will need to agree on a division of tasks in and out of the home according to abilities and preferences. These may change from time to time through the seasons of life. The couple will also need to find a way of reaching decisions that honour God together.

Adam was a man alone, a singleton. But in the company of Eve he became a race, a corporate body, and only then did he become capable of mirroring the true and full life of God, which is in the life of loving relationship.

Mike Mason,
The Mystery of Marriage

An example of perfect relationship

Gods Himself is the example for us of fitting together in a perfectly ordered and harmonious relationship: Father–Son–Spirit. God is three Persons mysteriously unified as one: as Tri-unity, or the Trinity. Each Person is equally God and yet the Son seeks to do the will of the Father,[22] and together, with the Father, sends out the Spirit.[23] So **God models to us a relationship of love and the way of other-centredness and submission.**

As husband and wife, God intends for us to be two equals unified as one. He puts Himself as the ultimate head in the divine ordering: God–husband–wife. **With God at the head and in the heart of our marriage we can reflect His image in a unique way that we can't as individuals, through the nature of our 'fitted together' relationship.**

This session looks at how we can grow closer when we live together in a way that complements one another.

Group Session

Feedback

- What insights or encouragements did you gain from your Couple Time following the session on 'deepening our physical and spiritual intimacy'?
- Was there anything in the Introductory Reading for this session about husbands and wives that prompted you to think about the subject in a new way? Explain.

A special note

This session is intended to unpack some core issues to do with men and women in marriage. It is not possible to cover every aspect or all the complexities. The intention is to explore some key ideas from the Bible to help husbands and wives decide how they will 'fit together' in their marriage in a way that honours God.

A How do we fit together as husbands and wives?

We all come into a marriage as imperfect people with individual identities as well as our own attitudes and behaviour patterns. When we marry we begin a life-long process of learning to fit together.

1. What does our culture tell men and women they need to be like in a marriage?[24] In what ways should or could a Christian marriage be different from society's view?

God's design principles

The first principle is that human beings were not meant to be alone.[25] In marriage we move from two independent beings to an interdependent relationship as one. **God intends for a husband and wife to live together as a united team, supporting one another with our individual skills, gifting and personality.**

The second principle is that together we are to reflect God's image in a unique way that we can't as individuals – through the nature of our relationship. **God illustrates the perfect**

relationship and divine order for us in the interpersonal relationship of Father–Son–Spirit. He wants us to mirror the key aspects of this kind of relationship in our marriage. Put simply, they are:

- **Equal value of each person**[26]
- **A divine order**[27]
- **Unity of purpose**[28]
- **Mutual submission and sacrificial love**[29]

Foundation Principle:
God intends for a husband and wife to live in a way that is complementary – NOT competing with each other.

ome men are born with :old feet; some acquire :old feet; and some have :old feet thrust upon them.
Anon

God's design principles need to be applied in a practical way so that we fit together in our everyday lives.

A How do we fit together as husbands and wives?

Complete part i of this Couple Time box now. Part ii can be completed later during your Couple Time.

i. Take a minute to jot down your answer to the following:

Think of a significant contribution your partner is making to the marriage. In what way(s) does he/she complement you?

- Write down something your partner does and/or the way they do it.
- Also write down an aspect of their character, which complements yours.

Then tell him/her what you wrote down.

Complete the following later in your Couple Time

ii. Consider how you and your partner complement one another as you carry out day-to-day responsibilities (*for some ideas see the table*). Issues can sometimes arise when both partners try to do the same thing or make assumptions about the role of the other. 'How do I feel about the way we fulfil our roles – do I work with you in a complementary way?' (*Tick the appropriate boxes in the table*)

Am I working in a complementary way with my partner? In the way we are …	**Yes – and** I'm happy with the way we fulfil our roles	**Yes – but** I'd like to talk about making some changes	**No – let's** find a better way of doing this together
Managing money	☐	☑	☐
Making significant decisions	☐	☑	☐
Managing the home	☐	☑	☐
Managing social/leisure time	☐	☑	☐
Raising children	☐	☑	☐
Caring for elderly relatives	☑	☐	☐
Other…	☐	☐	☐

In your Couple Time be prepared to discuss the areas where you are working well together. Also talk about any areas where you feel you would like to clarify your responsibilities so that you work together in a more complementary way.

B A marriage with God at the heart of it

God will help us to fit together in a marriage if we put Him at the heart of it. Often a husband and wife can be at different places on their spiritual journey, but wherever we are God can help us if we want Him to. **We do this by individually surrendering control to God – doing what God wants for our marriage instead of wanting our own way.** This yielding of our hearts and wills to Him is not a one-off event but a daily surrender or submission to the headship of Christ.

1. What would a marriage be like where both a husband and wife willingly submit to God – to the headship of Christ? Think of practical examples in terms of:
   - How a couple behave towards one another
   - How decisions are made
   - Managing time and money etc
2. Why is submission to God hard in a marriage? What part does the Holy Spirit play?

Note about submission:
ubmission is not an easy
ıbject in today's Western
ulture which prizes individual
ghts. It is vital to remember
ıat submission is something
'e choose to do. As Christians
'e yield or submit ourselves
rst to God – to Jesus and His
ivine authority. God does not
ırce us to submit to Him – it
something we do willingly
ecause we recognise
esus as Lord and respond
Him out of love. The Bible
so tells us to submit to one
nother out of reverence
r Christ. This means we are
ıbject to human authority
s long as it does not involve
sobedience to God. This is
ossible if we are filled with
od's Spirit and experience
e fruit of humility.

Foundation Principle:
God will help us to fit together as we submit our individual hearts and wills and our marriage to Him.

B A marriage with God at the heart at it

i. Are there any areas in my life where I am struggling to be fully submitted to and trusting in God? Eg:

- Time alone with God
- Bible reading and prayer
- Time with partner and family
- Money – spending it/earning it?
- Sex-life
- Personal ambition
- Other …

ii. How am I doing in living a Spirit-filled life? What, if anything, needs to change?

In your Couple Time be prepared to share your thoughts with your partner and pray for one another.

At this time men and women split into two separate groups.

Questions for MEN ONLY are on pages 130–132
and questions for WOMEN ONLY are on pages 133–136

MEN ONLY

C How does a husband fulfil his God-given role?

God intends marriage to be an equal partnership with complementary roles.

1. The way marriage partners relate to each other is vital to a flourishing marriage. Discuss the possible consequences to a marriage if either one of the partners is very dominating or very passive in the relationship.

Important messages for husbands and wives

The BIG PROBLEM for all relationships is that ever since the Fall we have been living with the consequences of the distortion of creation. In the case of husbands and wives this often results in things like: oppression, exploitation and manipulation, none of which are part of God's plan. Neither does He intend the relationship to be skewed out of balance, with one partner overly dominant and the other completely passive. God wants us to 'pull together' in the same direction.

Paul, the apostle, must have seen his fair share of marriage-related issues; he had important messages for husbands and wives in his letter to the Ephesians.

Bible study

21Submit to one another out of reverence for Christ.
22Wives, submit to your husbands as to the Lord. 23For the husband is the head of the wife as
Christ is the head of the church, his body, of which he is the Saviour. 24Now as the church
submits to Christ, so also wives should submit to their husbands in everything.
25Husbands, love your wives, just as Christ loved the church and gave himself up for her 26to
make her holy, cleansing her by the washing with water through the word, 27and to present
her to himself as a radiant church, without stain or wrinkle or any other blemish, but holy and

lote:
ubmission in marriage is
ot a role. The submission of
wife to her husband reflects
ne divinely-created order of:
God–husband–wife and so it
nust be seen in the context of
ne overall headship of Christ.
ubmission is a **free choice**.
cannot be forced. For a
vife, submission is a willing
ct of support and grows out
f an attitude of respect for
ne husband. It is easier for a
vife to submit to her husband
vhen she sees her husband
ehaving with Christlikeness in
ne home.

takes a smart husband to
ave the last word and not
se it.
Anon

blameless. [28]In this same way, husbands ought to love their wives as their own bodies. He
who loves his wife loves himself. [29]After all, no-one ever hated his own body, but he feeds
and cares for it, just as Christ does the church – [30]for we are members of his body. [31]"For
this reason a man will leave his father and mother and be united to his wife, and the two
will become one flesh." [32]This is a profound mystery – but I am talking about Christ and the
church. [33]However, each one of you also must love his wife as he loves himself, and the wife
must respect her husband.
Ephesians 5:21–33

2. God's plan for our marriages is to model the relationship between Christ and the Church.

a. What is the goal or purpose of a Christlike husband?

b. According to the passage, how is this achieved?

3. Why do you think some wives find it difficult to submit to their husbands? (Note: This question is not intended to probe the weaknesses of wives! Focus on the behaviour of husbands that may cause wives to struggle in giving respect and support.)

Principles for a Christlike husband

The purpose or goal of a Christlike husband is to enable his wife to fulfil her God-given potential to become BEAUTIFUL in character and behaviour. Growing in our role as a Christlike husband is a life-long process. In Ephesians 5 Paul gives the husband **three important aims – to be:**

- **Loving** – nourish and cherish his wife.
- **Sacrificial** – putting her needs first. Making her his first priority after God.
- **Proactive** – neither dominating nor passive, taking initiative; the emphasis is not on ruling, but on taking responsibility and offering care.

4. Look at the following case studies and questions.

Ben and Bella. *Bella wanted many things for herself and her family. Ben needed to work long hours to fulfil them. The bigger house was essential so the kids didn't have to share a room (the mortgage was only met by overtime). Holidaying for two weeks in the sun was vital in summer. Money was tight and the only way to cut costs was to get Ben to do all the DIY – hence THE LIST. Every weekend his time was scheduled to do all the jobs, which meant he had no leisure time or quality time with Bella and the kids. He understood the logic but sometimes it would have been so nice to go out for a beer with his mates or even enjoy a football match on the*

TV. The only space he did get was when Bella went out with her friends and after he had put the kids to bed. Ben was a quiet sort of person and Bella was lively and outgoing. Whenever he challenged the kids on their behaviour she would always take their side and accuse him of being too strict. After eighteen years of marriage Ben had settled in to 'going with the flow' instead of 'rocking the boat'.

a. Apply the principles of a Christlike husband, given the personality mixes. How could Ben relate better to Bella in ways that honour God?

Jake and Jane *married after a whirlwind romance. Jane was swept off her feet, but now four years later she felt like she had slipped into the role of Jake's mum. She did all the cooking and cleaning, even ironing his socks (just like his mum did)! Jake liked to make all the decisions. He lived life his way, seeing Jane as a pretty accessory on his arm when out with mates. Her needs as he saw them were to have a roof over her head and to be happy in homemaking. They didn't talk much – she knew better than to cross him. She seemed a willing participant in the bedroom although he was the one who would always initiate their love-making. He assumed that she was happy. More recently though he had begun to think that she was 'letting herself go a bit'.*

b. Apply the principles of a Christlike husband given the personality mixes. How could Jake relate better to Jane in ways that honour God?

Foundation Principle:
A husband fulfils his God-given role when he provides Christlike headship.

C How does a husband fulfil his God-given role?

i. One or two insights from the group discussion that I would like to share with my wife …

Discuss Christlike leadership

ii. In order to be a more Christlike husband I think I need to …

'pray + read more.

In your Couple Time be prepared to share your thoughts with your wife.

Margaret Thatcher's husband, Dennis, was once asked who wore the pants in his family. 'I do,' he replied. 'And I also wash and iron them.'

At this time men and women come together again. Please turn to page 136.

WOMEN ONLY

C How does a wife fulfil her God-given role?

God intends marriage to be an equal partnership with complementary roles.

1. The way marriage partners relate to each other is vital to a flourishing marriage. Discuss the possible consequences to a marriage if either one of the partners is very dominating or very passive in the relationship.

The only thing worse than a man you can't control is a man you can.
Margo Kaufman

Important messages for husbands and wives

The BIG PROBLEM for all relationships is that ever since the Fall we have been living with the consequences of the distortion of creation. In the case of husbands and wives this often results in things like oppression, exploitation and manipulation, none of which are part of God's plan. Neither does He intend the relationship to be skewed out of balance, with one partner overly dominant and the other completely submissive. God wants us to 'pull together' in the same direction.

Paul, the apostle, must have seen his fair share of marriage issues; he had important messages for husbands and wives in his letter to the Ephesians.

Bible study

21 Submit to one another out of reverence for Christ.
22 Wives, submit to your husbands as to the Lord. 23 For the husband is the head of the wife as
Christ is the head of the church, his body, of which he is the Saviour. 24 Now as the church
submits to Christ, so also wives should submit to their husbands in everything.
25 Husbands, love your wives, just as Christ loved the church and gave himself up for her 26 to
make her holy, cleansing her by the washing with water through the word, 27 and to present
her to himself as a radiant church, without stain or wrinkle or any other blemish, but holy and
blameless. 28 In this same way, husbands ought to love their wives as their own bodies. He
who loves his wife loves himself. 29 After all, no-one ever hated his own body, but he feeds
and cares for it, just as Christ does the church – 30 for we are members of his body. 31 "For

this reason a man will leave his father and mother and be united to his wife, and the two will become one flesh." [32]This is a profound mystery – but I am talking about Christ and the church. [33]However, each one of you also must love his wife as he loves himself, and the wife must respect her husband.
Ephesians 5:21–33

2. The passage says that the 'wife must respect her husband'.

a. Why is respecting a husband so important?

b. How does a wife show respect/disrespect?

Principles of a Christlike husband and a wife's response

The purpose or goal of a Christlike husband is to enable his wife to fulfil her God-given potential to become BEAUTIFUL in character and behaviour. This is a life-long process and Paul draws the attention of husbands to **three important aspects of a Christlike husband – to be:**

- **Loving** – nourishing and cherishing their wives.
- **Sacrificial** – putting her needs before his own. Making his wife his first priority after God.
- **Proactive** – neither dominating nor passive, taking initiative; the emphasis is not on ruling, but on responsibility and offering care.

The passage is **not** saying that a wife cannot take the initiative or a leading role in some areas of the marriage. It is **not** saying that a wife is a doormat or subservient. She is an equal partner in the marriage. It **is** telling wives to respond to their husbands in a way that respects and supports them, rather than undermining or criticising.

3. Paul emphasises a need for wives to submit to their husbands.

a. Does submission mean 'unthinking obedience'? What are the 'boundaries'?

b. How is a marriage affected by a wife who willingly submits to her husband's Christlike love and headship? How is it affected by a wife who doesn't willingly submit to her husband's loving headship?

c. Why do you think that some wives find it difficult to submit to their husbands? (Note: This question is not intended to probe the weaknesses of husbands! Focus on the things that some wives may be struggling with within themselves.)

Note:
Submission in marriage is not a role. The submission of a wife to her husband reflects the divinely created order of: God–husband–wife. Submission is a **free choice** we make. It **cannot be forced**. For a wife, submission is a willing act of support and grows out of an attitude of respect for the husband. It is easier for a wife to submit to her husband when she sees her husband behaving with Christlikeness in the home.

Principles to live by as a wife

Showing respect for her husband – honour, esteem and defer to him. Making him her first priority, after God.
Supporting her husband – working by his side using her unique talents and gifts so that together they fulfil God's purposes. An aspect of support is to willingly acknowledge his headship.
Love undergirds everything. Giving respect and support to a husband are not just the dry duty of a wife, but the out-workings of her love for her husband.

4. Look at the following case studies and questions.

Jake and Jane *married after a whirlwind romance. Jane was swept off her feet, but now four years later she felt like she had slipped into the role of Jake's mum. She did all the cooking and cleaning, even ironing his socks (just like his mum did)! Jake liked to make all the decisions. He lived life his way, seeing Jane as a pretty accessory on his arm when out with mates. Her needs as he saw them were to have a roof over her head and to be happy in homemaking. They didn't talk much – she knew better than to cross him. She seemed a willing participant in the bedroom although he was the one who would always initiate their love-making. He assumed that she was happy. More recently though he had begun to think that she was 'letting herself go a bit'.*

a. Apply the principles to live by as a wife given the personality mixes. How could Jane relate better to Jake in ways that honour God?

Ben and Bella. *Bella wanted many things for herself and her family. Ben needed to work long hours to fulfil them. The bigger house was essential so the kids didn't have to share a room (the mortgage was only met by overtime). Holidaying for two weeks in the sun was vital in summer. Money was tight and the only way to cut costs was to get Ben to do all the DIY – hence THE LIST. Every weekend his time was scheduled to do all the jobs, which meant he had no leisure time or quality time with Bella and the kids. He understood the logic but sometimes it would have been so nice to go out for a beer with his mates or even enjoy a football match on the TV. The only space he did get was when Bella went out with her friends and after he had put the kids to bed. Ben was a quiet sort of person and Bella was lively and outgoing. Whenever he challenged the kids on their behaviour she would always take their side and accuse him of being too strict. After eighteen years of marriage Ben had settled in to 'going with the flow' instead of 'rocking the boat'.*

b. Apply the principles to live by as a wife given the personality mixes. How could Bella relate better to Ben in ways that honour God?

Foundation Principle:
A wife fulfils her God-given role when she respects and supports her husband.

Why does a woman work ten years to change a man's habits and then complain that he's not the man she married?
Barbra Streisand

C How does a wife fulfil her God-given role?

i. One or two insights from the group discussion that I would like to share with my husband …

ii. In order to be a more supportive and respectful wife I think I need to …

In your Couple Time be prepared to share your thoughts with your husband.

At this time men and women come together again.

… And finally

Take a minute to review the Foundation Principles for the session.

If you have time share some of the highlights from your discussion.

Agree on a date in your diaries for your Couple Time:

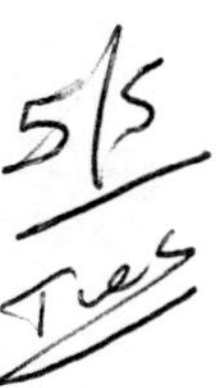

An archaeologist is the best husband a woman can have; the older she gets the more interested he is in her.

Agatha Christie

Note:
Be gentle with each other as you talk about this whole topic of fitting together. It is very easy for partners to feel unappreciated or criticised. Concentrate on affirming your partner. **If** there is change to be made then remember to **change yourself** and **don't try to change your partner!**

Couple Time – 60 minutes

A How do we fit together as husbands and wives?

If you did not have time to complete part **i** (page 128) then do it now. Talk about ways you complement one another.

Go on to complete part **ii**. Take a few minutes to individually tick the appropriate boxes. Then take turns telling each other where you placed ticks in the table for each area of responsibility. Affirm your partner for the things that they are doing well. Discuss any areas for possible change. (Note: Some of these responsibilities are big subjects in themselves. If either of you want to make significant changes you may wish to agree a separate time to revisit that particular area of responsibility – **don't try to fix everything now**.)

Identify a personal action point if needed.

Personal action point:
· Social/leisure time – discuss . . . productivity.

B A marriage with God at the heart at it

Share your answers to **i** (page 129) – any areas you are struggling to be fully submitted to God at the moment. Then share your answers to **ii** – how are you doing living the Spirit-filled life?

Identify a personal action point, if needed.

Personal action point:
[illegible] together trust/feeling.

C How does a husband/wife fulfil his/her God-given role?

Share your insights from the MEN only and WOMEN only discussions that were helpful to you (part **i**). Then, share your answers to part **ii** and remember to respond to your husband/wife with encouragement!
For husbands: this is what you feel you need to do to be a more Christlike husband.
For wives: this is what you feel you need to do to be a more supportive and respectful wife.

Identify a personal action point, if appropriate.

Personal action point:
- Attempt to show more respect/care.
- Bossy vs patient...

Praying together Pray for one another. (Note for husbands: if praying together is still unfamilar for you as a couple, then why not take the initiative to pray for your wife and your marriage now, silently or aloud together.)

At the next group meeting you will be asked to share one new insight you have gained about God's plan for husbands and wives to fit together in marriage. Agree upon what you would be prepared to share with the group from your Couple Time – maybe a different insight for each of you. Write them down:

Before the next group meeting please complete the Introductory Reading for Session 9: **Leaving a legacy that will last forever** (pages 141–143).Our lives are shaped by the influence of others, especially our families. The final session looks at how God wants our marriage to have a spiritual influence on people around us and on future generations.

NOTES
1. Ephesians 5:32.
2. Genesis 1:27 Man, Hebrew: *Ish*. Woman, Hebrew: *Ishah*, the feminine form of man's own name, because she came out of man.
3. The Hebrew phrase includes two words *ezer knegdo*. *Ezer* is translated 'helper' implying someone who assists, encourages and provides support for what is lacking in the one who needs help. The

For further reading:
Rocking the Roles, Robert Lewis and William Hendricks (Navpress, 1991) looks at biblical roles in marriage in a practical way.

Boundaries in Marriage, Dr Henry Cloud and Dr John Townsend (Zondervan, 1999) helps you understand and respect each other's needs, choices and freedom so you can give yourselves freely and lovingly to one another.

Celebration of Discipline, Richard Foster (Hodder & Stoughton, 1989). This excellent book guides you through the spiritual disciplines – those habits and practices that 'allow us to place ourselves before God so that He can transform us'.This edition includes a study guide help is then qualified by the word *knegdo*, so that it means a helper matching his eminence or perhaps his distinctiveness. It certainly points to one who is fit to stand before the man, opposite him as his counterpart, companion and complement. Literally the helper is 'like opposite him'. (*The Message of Genesis 1–11*, David Atkinson (IVP).)

4. Genesis 2:18–25.
5. Genesis 1:28.
6. *The Message of Ephesians*, John R.W. Stott (IVP, 1979).
7. The Greek for head is *Kephale*. The literal meaning is as a head governing a body. Like its Hebrew equivalent word, *rosh*, there is a metaphorical meaning as 'source' of a river or life. *Kephale* also refers to the concept of 'headship' which is the divine ordering of family, civic or ritual sphere of relationships. Headship carries authority – as delegated by God and therefore directly accountable to God. Jesus is head of the Church as its founder and sustainer. Christ wields authority as Lord and humbled Himself as servant. The New Testament references to the husband as head (Ephesians 5:23; 1 Corinthians 10:3) clearly state that headship means to be like Christ as Saviour. (*Expository Dictionary of Bible Words*, editor Stephen Renn (Hendrickson Publishers, ISBN 1 56563 938 3). *The Message of Ephesians*, John R.W. Stott (IVP).
8. www.comedy-zone.net
9. Mark 10:42–45; 1 Corinthians 11:3; Ephesians 1:22; 4:15; 5:23; Colossians 1:18; 2:9–10; 2:19.
10. John 15:12–14.
11. Ephesians 5:23–29; 1 Timothy 5:8.
12. Exodus 18:4; Deuteronomy 33:7,26; Psalm 20:2; 33:20; 115:9; 146:5.
13. Ephesians 5:22,33; 1 Peter 3:1–5.
14. Ephesians 2:13–18.
15. Ephesians 5:8–18; Romans 8:7.
16. Ecclesiastes 4:12.
17. Ephesians 5:21.
18. Ephesians 5:25.
19. Ephesians 5:24.
20. Christopher Ash, *Marriage. Sex in the Service of God* (IVP, 2003), Part 3:14.
21. 1 Timothy 5:8.
22. Matthew 26:39; Mark 14:36; Luke 22:42; John 4:34; 5:30; 6:38; 8:28–29; 12:49–50; 13:30; 15:10; Ephesians 5:22; 1 Corinthians 15:24–28.
23. John 14:26; 15:26.
24. Adapted from Question 1 Session 5 of *Building Your Marriage* Dennis Rainey (Group Publishing Copyright 2000 Dennis Rainey). Used with permission.
25. Genesis 2:18.
26. Genesis 1:27; Galatians 3:26–27.
27. 1 Corinthians 11:3; Ephesians 5:23.
28. Genesis 1:26–28; Genesis 2:24; Mark 10:6–9; John 17:20–23.
29. Ephesians 5:21–33; John 13:34–35.

9 Leaving a legacy that will last forever

Introductory Reading

When God created Adam and Eve He blessed them and instructed them to 'fill the earth'. Yet this was much more than a command to increase the human population by having children, which is good news for couples struggling to conceive. He was sending them on a life mission to reproduce His image through godly people. We can only do that as we get to know Him, and then help to make Him known to others.

Knowing God

It is part of our design as humans to know God and be known by Him.

He has made everything beautiful in its time. He has also set eternity in the hearts of men …
Ecclesiastes 3:11

We find meaning and purpose in life through a relationship with the eternal, living God. As we get to know God and the love He has for us, we are changed:

I. **We are set free.** We become more ourselves because God's unconditional love and acceptance free us to be the people He intends us to be. He can then shape our unique qualities, talents and experiences for the good – benefiting us and those around us.

II. **We are transformed.** We grow more into God's image, or likeness. Not that we become clones or robots, but our character and behaviour gradually become more like His, through the activity of His Spirit working in us.

III. **Our marriage is transformed.** When we open our marriage up to God He builds an ever-strengthening relationship of intimacy and trust, held together with sacrificial love and mutual submission. We become stronger together than the sum of our individual strengths.

Making God known

God wants all people to come to Him and love Him.[1] If we are in step with Him, He will use us to draw others, including our children if we have them, to seek God for themselves.

Others will see God in us when we live godly, loving lives and give Him the credit. He wants us to stand out as 'salt and light',[2] so that our lifestyles influence society. The apostle Peter encouraged Christian wives to 'win over' non-believing husbands through godly behaviour.[3] Christian husbands may similarly affect a non-believing wife. **God's desire is to shape every aspect of our married lives to be distinct, reflecting His image through the nature of our love for one another.** By loving each other in God's way we point to the source, just as Jesus in loving sacrificially pointed the way to God.

'A new command I give you: Love one another. As I have loved you, so you must love one another. By this all men will know that you are my disciples, if you love one another.'
John 13:34,35

Christ-centred living is important. Faith without action is empty,[4] even hypocritical. But living out the Christian life is not enough. **We need to introduce people to Jesus by telling them His message of love and forgiveness, because otherwise they won't know.** It's also worth remembering that telling people about God's love is an expression of love for them.

Many Christians find they are enthusiastic about sharing their experiences of God. Others are cautious and some hold back in fear. **Our marriage affects our willingness to witness, and our effectiveness as well.** If our marriage is a struggle we may feel we have nothing about God to commend to others. But Jesus was quite clear that He wanted His followers to actively spread God's message of love. In the 'Great Commission'[5] He charged His followers to tell people the good news about Himself.

A Christian is a keyhole through which other folk see God.
Robert E. Gibso

How did I come to know God? Was it through a parent, friend, minister ...? What was it about them that drew me to seek God or know Him more deeply?

*This commission was given to **every** follower of Jesus, not to pastors and missionaries alone. This is **your** commission from Jesus, and it's not optional. These words of Jesus are not the Great Suggestion.*
Rick Warre
The Purpose Driven Lif

What am I working for?
What do I want to be
remembered for?

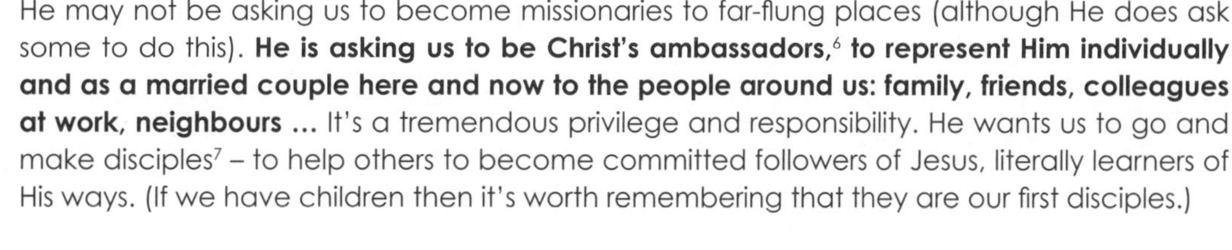

He may not be asking us to become missionaries to far-flung places (although He does ask some to do this). **He is asking us to be Christ's ambassadors,[6] to represent Him individually and as a married couple here and now to the people around us: family, friends, colleagues at work, neighbours …** It's a tremendous privilege and responsibility. He wants us to go and make disciples[7] – to help others to become committed followers of Jesus, literally learners of His ways. (If we have children then it's worth remembering that they are our first disciples.)

You two are always so sweet. You must be vegetarians

Rodney and Mabel realised that it was time to set the record straight about their faith

Married couples who unite together to love God, love others and tell them about His love, will leave a lasting spiritual legacy. It's an exciting way to live – experiencing abundant life together now and building something that lasts forever.[8]

This session looks at how we can have a spiritual influence on people around us and on future generations.

Group Session

Feedback

- What insights or encouragements did you gain from your Couple Time following the session on fitting together as husbands and wives?
- Was there anything in the Introductory Reading for this session about our legacy that prompted you to think about marriage in a new way? Explain.

A Understanding our different legacies

Our lives are deeply influenced by the words and actions of other people. When we look back we are able to recognise the lasting impact on our lives of parents, friends, teachers, neighbours etc. We too influence those we come into contact with.[9]

1. What kind of legacy have you been left? (Think about the influence of parents, friends, teachers etc.) How do you feel about this legacy?

Foundation Principle:
The legacy you pass on is more important than the legacy you were given.

A Understanding our different legacies

i. As I look back at the legacy I have been handed, is there anything I would like to thank my parents, other people or God for? Is there anyone I need to forgive or anyone of whom I need to ask forgiveness? (Make a note of it now.)

· parents respect for individuals views. · S's parents + friends Pope...

ii. What aspect of that legacy do I want to pass on? What do I not want to pass on?

· love
· God's love...

In your Couple Time be prepared to talk about your answers.

After a good dinner one ca forgive anybody, even one own relations.

Oscar Wild

B Leaving a spiritual legacy

In the creation account God tells Adam and Eve to 'fill' the earth.[10] His desire was for them to have children, but His instruction is about more than just increasing the numbers of humans on earth. **God wants to fill the earth with His image through the words, influence and actions of those who know Him personally.**

Bible study

36 'Teacher, which is the greatest commandment in the Law?' 37 Jesus replied: '"Love the Lord
your God with all your heart and with all your soul and with all your mind." 38 This is the first
and greatest commandment. 39 And the second is like it: "Love your neighbour as yourself."
40 All the Law and the Prophets hang on these two commandments.'
Matthew 22:36–40

1. How can we put the Great Commandment into practice as a couple?

- How can we show love for God in and through our marriage?

- How can we show love for others as a married couple? Think of some practical ideas.

2. Is it enough simply to live out our faith through actions?

Living and telling

Actions do speak louder than words. Faith is empty without action. However, if we don't tell people about our faith they might commend us for being good people, but probably not make the connection that God is the source. **To connect people with the source of love and hope we need to point them to God**. Just as we have received God's unconditional love, He wants us to pass it on by sharing the gospel message with others. Helping others, including our children, to know God – ie making Him known – is the mission He has given each believer.

Bible study

18 Then Jesus came to them and said, 'All authority in heaven and on earth has been given
to me. 19 Therefore go and make disciples of all nations, baptising them in the name of the

Father and of the Son and of the Holy Spirit, [20]and teaching them to obey everything I have commanded you. And surely I am with you always, to the very end of the age.'
Matthew 28:18–20

3. This 'Great Commission' was among some of Jesus' last words to His disciples and a vital part of His legacy. Think of ideas for helping to fulfil the Great Commission as a couple.

Foundation Principle:
God intends us to have a lasting spiritual impact as a couple by passing on God's love to our children and other people, through the things we say and do.

Your life is like a coin – you can spend it any way you want, but you can only spend it once.
Juan Carlos Orti
Argentinean Pastc

B Leaving a spiritual legacy

i. What do I most want to be remembered for?
· father · listening · love. (impatience, anger.

ii. What would I like our spiritual legacy to be? · Submit to God & His Spirit
· love · pointing to God
· peace · living with the Holy Spirit · Sharing God's love
· walking in God's way forever.

In your Couple Time be prepared to talk about your answers and anything you could do together to build a spiritual legacy.

C Sharing our faith

Showing that God is real and sharing our faith means more than asking people to come along to church. It's important to be able to speak about Jesus and God's love in a natural way.

/isit www.togetherinmarriage.
:om. **Together Notes:**
;haring Our Faith – Anything
o Declare? has more about
ıow to share our faith journey
vith others.

Bible study

1. What principles for sharing our faith in Christ does the following Bible passage give?

[2]Devote yourselves to prayer, being watchful and thankful. [3]And pray for us, too, that God
may open a door for our message, so that we may proclaim the mystery of Christ, for which
I am in chains. [4]Pray that I may proclaim it clearly, as I should. [5]Be wise in the way you act
towards outsiders; make the most of every opportunity. [6]Let your conversation be always full
of grace, seasoned with salt, so that you may know how to answer everyone.
Colossians 4:2–6

Stories from our lives

A simple and effective way of expressing our faith is through sharing parts of our spiritual journey:

- my attitude and approach to life before coming to faith
- why and how I came to trust in Jesus Christ
- how He has changed my life, including my marriage. You can talk about the difference God makes in your life even if you have always had a faith in Jesus.

only God would give me
ɔme clear sign! Like making
large deposit in my name
a Swiss bank.
Woody Allen

People are interested in other people's lives. Also, others can identify with us and learn of the impact God has on our lives through Jesus Christ, if we are prepared to tell them about Him.

2. What keeps people from sharing about their spiritual journey? Think of some ideas which might help people to explain to non-Christians about the impact God has had on their lives.

Foundation Principle:
Those around us will see the reality of God when we live out and talk of the **difference** He has made in our lives.

C Sharing our faith

i. What insights from the discussion could help me share my faith with other people? Write down one or two insights.

ii. What one thing could I tell a non-Christian about the difference God makes to my marriage?

iii. Who are the people God wants me to influence for Him? Write down the names of five people (or couples) you can pray for regularly that they will come to know Jesus personally.

In your Couple Time be prepared to talk about your answers and anything you could do together to share your faith.

The single greatest gift you can give someone is an introduction to God.

Bill Hybels

A Walk Across a Room

… And now

Take a minute to review the Foundation Principles for the session.

Agree on a date for your diaries for your Couple Time:

Feedback

As an individual, take a few minutes to write down your answers to the following questions:

a. What new insight have I gained about God and marriage as a result of these sessions?

b. What is one specific way God is making a difference in my marriage as a result of *Together* – something that I am doing differently?

c. What has this group meant to me during the course of the study?

Note:
You can complete this feedback section[11] and 'What next?' now or they could be done separately at another time, maybe at a celebration supper.

As a couple: Briefly talk about your answers to the questions and agree on the things you are prepared to share with the rest of the group. (Remember you can pass on any of the questions if you wish.)

Then, as a group: listen to each other's comments.

What next?

There are several options to consider as a group about what you could do next (and you can select more than one option):

a. Continuing to meet as the same group to do another study (there are ideas in Further Resources: Additional resources for small groups on www.togetherinmarriage.com).
b. Taking some new initiatives as a whole group (or as a couple) in evangelism and discipleship (see Further Resources on our website for resources to help you).
c. If you have benefited from being part of this group, then why not share those benefits with other couples and consider starting another *Together* group?
d. Finishing *Together* and not going on with the current group.

... And finally

Close with a time of prayer. You might want to consider the following as you pray together:

- giving thanks for the ways our relationship has benefited
- asking God to show us ways to touch the family lives of other people with God's love and share our faith with them

Couple Time – 60 minutes

Love does not consist in gazing at each other, but in looking outward together in the same direction.
Antoine de Saint-Exupery

As you talk to each other **remember the dos and don'ts of listening.**

A Understanding our different legacies

Tell each other about the legacies you were handed and how you feel about them, sharing your answers to **i** on page 144. Then share your answers to question **ii**.

Identify a personal action point, if necessary.

Personal action point:

B Leaving a spiritual legacy

Share your answers to question **i** (page 146). Then talk about what you would like your spiritual legacy to be.

Consider starting another *Together* group as part of your spiritual legacy as a couple. If you want to start another group then think about/pray for couples you could ask to join a new group.

Identify a personal action point, if applicable.

Personal action point:

Take time together to visit www.togetherinmarriage.com and look at **Together Notes: Sharing Our Faith – Anything to Declare?** and think through how you would each describe your spiritual journey.

For further reading;
Why and How Should We Tell Others? Nicky Gumbel (Kingsway Communications Ltd, 2005). A helpful booklet with content taken from the book *Alpha – Questions of Life*.

Just Walk Across the Room, Bill Hybels (Zondervan, 2006). An excellent book on taking a natural relational approach in personal evangelism that follows Jesus' example.

Why not visit our website and look at **Further Resources** together for ideas of what to do next.

C Sharing our faith

What things encourage you to share your faith? What ideas can you help each other put into action?

Share the insights you gained from the discussion which could help you share your faith or share it more regularly or with more people. Could you tell a non-Christian about the difference God makes to your marriage? (Questions **i** and **ii** page 148).
Identify an action point.

Personal action point:

There are optional additional questions overleaf for couples with children.

What next?

Share your thoughts with your partner and agree how you will respond to the following:

Do we wish to continue meeting with the current group? Yes / No
Do we want to consider starting a *Together* group ourselves? Yes / No

What would we like to do next? Write down ideas and preferences:

Praying together

- Give thanks to God together in prayer for parents and other people and the positive impact they have had on your lives.
- Pray for forgiveness and healing if there are wounds from the past that are still hurting.
- Thank God for one another and your marriage – for what He has done and what He will do!
- Ask God to show you who you could share your faith with. Pray for those five people or couples you noted in Couple Time prep **C iii** (p.148) and ask God to prepare their hearts to be receptive to His love and gospel message.

For couples with children

(optional additional questions)

i. Look at the following Bible passages together. Note down any thoughts about what kind of legacy God wants you to leave your children and how you can do this[12]

[1]Praise the LORD.
Blessed is the man who fears the LORD,
who finds great delight in his commands.
[2]His children will be mighty in the land;
the generation of the upright will be blessed.
Psalm 112:1–2

I have been reminded of your sincere faith, which first lived in your grandmother Lois and in your mother Eunice and, I am persuaded, now lives in you also.
2 Timothy 1:5

[4]Hear, O Israel: The LORD our God, the LORD is one. [5]Love the LORD your God with all your heart
and with all your soul and with all your strength. [6]These commandments that I give you
today are to be upon your hearts. [7]Impress them on your children. Talk about them when
you sit at home and when you walk along the road, when you lie down and when you get
up. [8]Tie them as symbols on your hands and bind them on your foreheads. [9]Write them on
the door-frames of your houses and on your gates.
Deuteronomy 6:4–9

ii. Agree on one thing you could do as a family to help nurture the faith of your family unit.

NOTES

1. 2 Peter 3:8–15.
2. Matthew 5:13–16.
3. 1 Peter 3:1.
4. James 2:14–25.
5. Matthew 28:19–20; Mark 16:15; Luke 24:47; John 20:21; Acts 1:8.
6. 2 Corinthians 5:20.
7. Matthew 28:19–20.
8. Romans 8:37–39; 1 Corinthians 3.
9. The heart of section A of this session of *Together*, including the first Foundation Principle, is based on Session 7 of *Building Your Marriage* by Dennis Rainey (Group Publishing Copyright © 2000). Used with permission.
10. Genesis 1:28.
11. This last feedback section of *Together* is adapted from 'wrap up' Session 7, *Building Your Marriage* op. cit. Used with permission.
12. Adapted from questions 5 and 6 of Session 7, *Building Your Marriage*, op. cit. Used with permission.

Knowing God

Entering into a relationship with God is the beginning of a new life. Before we can begin this new spiritual life we have to deal with a big problem.[1]

The BIG problem

Couples who want a strong and flourishing marriage, work to resolve their problems in the areas of communication, money, sexuality and so on. However, there is one basic problem at the heart of every marriage, and it's a problem we can't fix. No matter how hard we try, this problem is too big to deal with on our own.

The big problem is we are cut off from God. **If we want to experience our marriage the way it was designed to be we need a vital relationship with God, who offers us the power to live a life of joy and purpose**. But we are disconnected from this power.

What separates us from God is sin. Many of us assume that the term sin refers to actions which most of us agree are wrong. We try to deal with the problem of our sin by working hard to become better people. But within our hearts we know our sin problem runs much deeper than a list of bad habits. **All of us have chosen to go our own way instead of God's; we may openly rebel against God, or simply ignore Him**. It is this self-centred attitude that the Bible calls sin.

We are all the same: *'for all have sinned and fall short of the glory of God,'* (Romans 3:23). God is perfect (**holy**), we are sinful, so there is a great spiritual gap between us. We may try to feel better through work, relationship, sport or religion. But all our attempts fail because we have ignored the real problem – turning our backs on God.

The amazing solution

God is holy, but He is also **loving**. So He took the initiative to restore a relationship with us by showing us 'grace' (undeserved forgiveness and acceptance).[2] As well as being holy and loving, God is also **just** and so there is a price that has to be paid for our sin.

God took on human form in the Person of Jesus Christ. He lived a holy life, in perfect obedience to God's will. Jesus, being without sin Himself, took the punishment we deserved by dying on the cross in our place. Jesus died willingly to satisfy God's justice and restore our relationship with God.

For the wages of sin is death, but the gift of God is eternal life in Christ Jesus our Lord.
Romans 6:23

But God demonstrates his own love for us in this: While we were still sinners, Christ died for us.
Romans 5:8

Paul, the apostle tells us that, '… Christ died for our sins according to the Scriptures, that he was buried, that he was raised on the third day according to the Scriptures, and that he appeared to Peter, and then to the Twelve. After that, he appeared to more than five hundred …'
1 Corinthians 15:3–6

God's answer to the problem of sin is a gift – we cannot earn it and we don't deserve it. Jesus Christ is unique[3] (both human and God). He died in our place so that our relationship with God can be restored and we can have eternal life[4]. God proved His power and authority by raising Jesus to life again[5] **Jesus gave His life so that we might be pardoned and have an eternal relationship with God** – giving us hope for life in this world and beyond the grave.

The critical decision

This gift is available to all who desire a personal relationship with God. Jesus gives us this picture: *'Here I am! I stand at the door and knock. If anyone hears my voice and opens the door, I will come in and eat with him, and he with me.'* (Revelation 3:20)

God has promised that if we agree that we have turned our backs on Him, He will forgive us and resolve our sin problem.

Yet to all who received him, to those who believed in his name, he gave the right to become children of God
John 1:12

For it is by grace you have been saved, through faith – and this not from yourselves, it is the gift of God – not by works, so that no-one can boast.
Ephesians 2:8–9

When the Bible talks about receiving Christ, it means agreeing with God that we are sinners and can't fix the problem ourselves. It means turning away from sin – our self-centred way of life. And it means trusting God to forgive our sins. It's not enough to just intellectually believe that Jesus Christ is the Son of God. It is an inner turning of our heart and mind towards trusting Jesus as our Saviour (the one who rescues us because we cannot save ourselves).

To experience a personal relationship with God we need to:

- **accept responsibility for our own sin and agree that we are totally cut off from God**
- **inwardly turn to God and trust Him to forgive us completely, because Jesus has paid the price for our sin**
- **live our lives with Jesus Christ at the centre (rather than 'our'selves).**

We can do this by talking to God in prayer, remembering that He is not so concerned with our words as our attitude. In the box there is a suggested prayer…

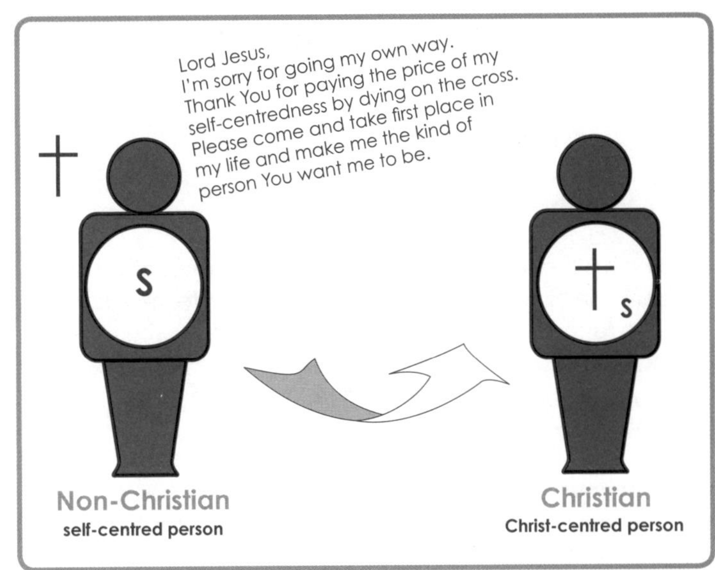
Lord Jesus,
I'm sorry for going my own way.
Thank You for paying the price of my
self-centredness by dying on the cross.
Please come and take first place in
my life and make me the kind of
person You want me to be.
S
S
Non-Christian
self-centred person
Christian
Christ-centred person

The new reality

We enter into a new relationship with God based on His grace[6] and not our performance. Like a precious diamond, God's saving grace has many facets:

1. We are free from the condemnation of sin, guilt, shame, death and evil powers.
2. We have new life in all its fullness as God intended,[7] and can experience His unconditional love, giving us joy, peace, wholeness, security and heaven.
3. We are indwelt by God's Holy Spirit (His intimate presence) to help, strengthen and guide us.[8]
4. We are assured that God will never leave us.[9]
5. We benefit from God's complete forgiveness.[10]
6. As we live in the light of God's grace He enables us to show grace to others. Our ability to forgive others is linked to our having experienced God's forgiveness.

How can we be really sure all this has happened?

If we have sincerely opened our heart to Jesus Christ, we can know that He is in our life because God has promised this and can be trusted.

And this is the testimony: God has given us eternal life, and this life is in his Son. He who has the Son has life; he who does not have the Son of God does not have life. I write these things to you who believe in the name of the Son of God so that you may know that you have eternal life.
1 John 5:11–13

For I am convinced that neither death nor life, neither angels nor demons, neither the present nor the future, nor any powers, neither height nor depth, nor anything else in all creation, will be able to separate us from the love of God that is in Christ Jesus our Lord.
Romans 8:38–39

We can always rely on God and His promises in the Bible. But we cannot always rely on our feelings because they come and go. **The Christian lives by faith (trust) in the trustworthiness of God Himself and His Word**, the Bible (God's promises).

Flying in an airplane can illustrate the relationship between faith and feelings. To be transported by an airplane we must place our faith in the trustworthiness of the aircraft and the pilot who flies it. Our feelings of confidence or fear do not affect the ability of the airplane to transport us, though they do affect how much we enjoy the trip.

In the same way, as Christians we know that our relationship with God does not depend on our feelings or emotions, but on our faith (trust) in the trustworthiness of God Himself and the promises of His word in the Bible.

Suggestions for Christian GROWTH

Our faith in God grows as we trust God with every detail of our lives. We will find it helpful to:

- **G**et to know God by reading the Bible (2 Timothy 3:14–17)
- **R**espond to God in prayer (Philippians 4:6)
- **O**bey God moment by moment (Luke 6:46–49)
- **W**alk in the power of the Holy Spirit (Colossians 2:6; Ephesians 3:14—21; 5:18)
- **T**ell others about Jesus Christ by the life we lead and the words we say. (Matthew 28:18–20; 2 Corinthians 5:17–20; Ephesians 4:1)
- **H**ave contact with other Christians. (Hebrews 10:25; Acts 2:42–47)

NOTES

1. Adapted from the following sources:
 'Our problem, God's answers', *'Building Your Marriage'*. Group Publishing Copyright c 2000 Dennis Rainey. Used with permission.
 'Knowing God personally', Agape Ministries Ltd. Copyright 1976, 1985, 1994, 1196, 1998, 2000, 2001.
2. Ephesians 2:8,9
3. John 14:6
4. John 3:16, John 17:3
5. 1Corinthians 15
6. John 1:12, Romans 8:12-25, Ephesians 1:5
7. John 10:10
8. John 14:15-27
9. Romans 8:37-39
10. Ephesians 4:32, Colossians 3:13